Hurtling into a Void

Hurtling into a Void

Transition to adulthood for young disabled people with 'complex health and support needs'

Jenny Morris

RESEARCH *INTO* PRACTICE

RESEARCH *INTO* PRACTICE

Hurtling into a Void

**Transition to adulthood for young disabled people
with 'complex health and support needs'**

Jenny Morris

Published for the Joseph Rowntree Foundation by Pavilion Publishing (Brighton) Ltd
Pavilion Publishing (Brighton) Ltd.
8 St George's Place
Brighton, East Sussex BN1 4GB

Telephone: 01273 623222

Fax: 01273 625526

Email: pavpub@pavilion.co.uk

Web: www.pavpub.com

The Joseph Rowntree Foundation
The Homestead
40 Water End, York YO3 6LP

Telephone: 01904 629241

First published 1999.

ISBN 1 84196 001 2

Editor: Liz Mandeville

Design and typesetting: Stanford Douglas

Cover illustration: Angela Martin

Printing: Paterson Printing (Tunbridge Wells)

Contents

Acknowledgements

The most important people who contributed to this report were the fourteen young people and two parents who shared their experiences. Various people from six local authorities were good enough to give me verbal and written information about their policies. Unfortunately, like the young people and parents, they were assured anonymity so I cannot name them.

I would also like to thank Susan Hemmings for carrying out some of the interviews with young people and to the following people who provided me with information about their own work or helped in other ways:

Nat Bennett

Jane Cooper, Long Term Medical Conditions Alliance

Lynette Couldridge, The National Society for Epilepsy

Jan Cunningham, St Margaret's School

Barry Hayward, Arthritis Care

Nicola Hendey

Margaret Huxtable, Dorincourt Centre

Gill Levy, RNIB

Neil Miller, SeeAbility

Gill Moss, Association of Youth with ME

Gill Norris, PINNT Support group for patients receiving parenteral or enteral nutrition therapy

Jean Pownceby, Cystic Fibrosis Trust

Karen Shaw, Psychosocial Rheumatology Research Centre, Coventry

Tom Shakespeare

Janice Simons

Fiona Street, Leonard Cheshire Foundation

Thanks also to Nina Evans at The British Library.

Introduction

Over the last few years, there has been growing awareness of children and young people who cannot be neatly slotted into the traditional service categories of 'physical and sensory disability' and 'learning disability'. There appears to be an increasing number of children and young people who have a range of physical, sensory and cognitive impairments, many of whom also have continuing health care needs associated with their impairments. There are also children and young people who, while they do not have a number of impairments, have quite high levels of need for continuing health care. These include young people with cystic fibrosis, myalgic encephalomyelitis (ME), haemoglobinopathies (sickle cell disorder or thalassaemia) and gastrostomies, and some of those who have survived childhood cancer. In recent years, children with conditions associated with poor life expectancy have been surviving into adulthood and, in some instances, into middle and even old age, because of more effective interventions and better quality care.

Services are divided into health, social care, education, housing and so on, yet it is not always easy to so divide young people's needs. Health and social services are also divided into children's and adults' services, and according to diagnosis and 'client' groups. This can further complicate matters for young people as they grow into adulthood. If increasing numbers of children are surviving with 'multiple impairments' and/or continuing health care needs, then we need to know more about their transition into adulthood and how well policies and practices are meeting their needs.

This review aims to summarise what we know from existing research about transition to adulthood for young people with 'health and support needs'. Information was also gathered from six local authority social services departments on policies concerning this group, including joint work with health and education services. The report includes, as well, material from fourteen accounts by young people of their experiences and aspirations and two accounts by parents of young people who have significant learning and communication difficulties. These first-hand accounts cover a wide range of conditions and situations, yet there are clear common messages from these young people.

Part 1 of the report discusses what is meant by 'complex health and support needs' and 'transition to adulthood'. It sets the context, looking at what we know about the number of young people who might fall under the general heading of having 'complex health and support needs'. **Part 2** summarises existing research, and includes information gathered from the six local authorities that were consulted during the course of this work.

Part 2 also includes information about 16 young people who have a range of experiences, but all of whom have health and support needs that service providers have sometimes found difficult to meet. The ages of the young people ranged from

17 to 29. They were all contacted through service providers and voluntary organisations.

Some of the accounts started off as a piece of writing by the young person, in response to a set of questions sent to them. Other young people were interviewed. A number of the young people have communication impairments (two of them do not use speech and a number have limited vocabularies). In two cases, the young person's level of impairment was such that it was not possible to ask them about their past experiences, so their mothers were interviewed.

Each person was asked the same questions about their experiences of the transition to adulthood, with particular reference to their contact with health, education and social services, but they each elaborated on these issues in different ways, or sometimes they had little to say on an issue.

The interviews were transcribed and edited to form an account by the young person. They were then sent a copy, so that they could add, amend or delete anything. Some were visited a second time to discuss their account. Each account was agreed by the young person (or, in two cases, by the parent) concerned. Names and any other identifying information have been changed. Unless the young person referred to his/her condition or impairment themselves, information is not given about this when using extracts from their accounts.

This report is aimed primarily at those responsible for commissioning and providing services to young people with high levels of health and support needs during their transition to adulthood. The Department of Health's discussion document, *Partnership in Action*, concluded that joint working between health and social services is needed at three levels:

● strategic planning

● service commissioning

● service provision.

(Department of Health, 1998a, p6)

Throughout this report, questions are highlighted for those working at all these three levels, in the hope that it will help them to focus on the things that will assist young people with 'complex health and support needs' to make a successful transition to adulthood. These questions are also listed at the end of the report.

Part One

Definitions and numbers

Before looking at the messages from research, we need to be clear about what experiences are included in the terms 'complex health and support needs' and 'transition to adulthood'.

What do we mean by 'complex health and support needs'?

The social model of disability separates out 'disability' and 'impairment', and this helps us to define what is meant by the term 'health and support needs'. 'Impairment' means the functional limitations of someone's body or mind as measured against a notional norm or average. The word therefore refers to a wide range of experiences, such as the functional limitations arising from conditions like cerebral palsy (impaired mobility, co-ordination, speech), cystic fibrosis (impaired lung function and digestive system) or autism (impaired ability to relate to others, impaired language).

People who experience impairments, and those who care about them, often search for and get some comfort from obtaining a diagnosis, a reason, which might explain their experience of their bodies and minds. However, diagnosis in itself does not determine either the level of impairment or its consequences for any particular individual. Gathering information about how many people in the population have, for example, brain injury or sickle cell anaemia does not, therefore, tell us enough about what kinds of need exist, although it will give a starting point.

The social model takes 'disability' to refer to disabling barriers experienced by individuals with impairments. These barriers are caused by other people's and society's reactions to these functional limitations. These barriers, or disenabling factors, fall into two general categories:

- inadequate and/or unequal access to the things necessary for a good quality of life
- prejudicial attitudes held by others arising from their reactions to impairment.

Together, these two sets of barriers cut disabled people off from inclusion in mainstream life. They are inevitably barriers to both human and civil rights.

People with impairments may be disabled by unequal access to the things that everyone needs for a good quality life – things such as adequate housing, employment and leisure activities – and/or they may be disabled by inadequate access to the additional things that they need in order to meet their needs arising from impairment – mobility equipment, appropriate medication, physiotherapy, etc.

The social model of disability is as concerned with equal and appropriate access to health care as it is with equal and appropriate access to education. Someone with cystic fibrosis will be disabled (the quality of their life will be diminished) by poor access to the health care they need, just as someone with autism will be disabled by unequal access to education.

The social model has a holistic approach. It recognises that, while someone with continuing health care needs and/or 'multiple impairments' may require a complex support plan, their needs remain the same, and should be given the same respect, as everyone else's. Describing people's health and support needs as 'complex' may be inappropriate, because there is a danger of treating someone's needs as the problem, whereas the problem is the barriers they experience to getting their needs met. This report has used the term 'complex health and support needs' in the title as a way of alerting its audience to what the report covers. Policy-makers and professionals tend to use the term 'complex health and support needs', but it is not really people's needs which are 'complex'; rather, the systems and services they have to negotiate to get their needs met are complex. The report will try to be explicit about people's needs, their impairments and the disabling barriers they experience.

While carrying out interviews and reviewing research for this report, we gathered information about young people who fall within the following descriptions (some come under more than one category):

- people with physical/sensory/communication impairments and high levels of support needs

- people with physical/sensory/communication impairments and/or learning difficulties

- people with physical/sensory/communication impairments and/or learning difficulties and mental health needs

- people with physical/sensory/communication impairments and/or learning difficulties, and challenging behaviours

- people with significant learning difficulties

- people with compromised health and life expectancy arising from conditions such as cystic fibrosis

- people with chronic conditions such as ME, epilepsy or sickle cell anaemia

- people whose experience of cancer or other disease has left them with continuing health care and/or support needs.

On the one hand, the above list obviously covers a huge range of experiences, and it might seem inappropriate to attempt to put them all into a general category of 'complex health and support needs'. On the other hand, it has become evident that there are a number of common experiences shared by these groups of people, in terms of both their general transition to adulthood and their relationships with services. A key common characteristic is that they all require a combination of health and support services in order to access a good quality of life, and that existing services seem to find it a complex matter to meet their needs. These young people are particularly vulnerable to a failure of health and social services to meet their needs during the transition to adulthood. This is a key disabling barrier that they share.

What do we mean by 'transition to adulthood'?

The term 'transition to adulthood' refers to both a particular stage of life experiences and to experiences of services. In terms of life experiences, transition to adulthood is said to involve:

- transition from school to training, employment or unemployment

- moving out of the parents'/carers' home

- transition to adult sexuality, coupledom, marriage and possibly parenthood

- financial independence from parents (or other carers).

(Barnardo's, 1996, p9)

Generally, young people from the age of 16 to their early 20s are thought of as being in transition to adulthood. In service terms, young people are usually referred from children's to adults' health and social services between the ages of 16 and 18. For those who have a statement of special educational need (SSEN), the education authority has a duty to include a Transition Plan in the first annual review of a young person's SSEN after the age of 14, and this Transition Plan must be reviewed every year until the young person leaves school. The education authority must also refer the young person to their social services authority, which must then decide whether they come under the legal definition of 'disabled person' (*Disabled Persons Act 1986*). This procedure should lead to an assessment of the young person's needs under the *Chronically Sick and Disabled Persons Act 1970* and, if required, access to support provided by the social services department's community care services.

Transition to adulthood is a time of change, and it should be a time of growing independence. However, a survey of young disabled people, which also compared their experiences with their non-disabled peers, concluded that between 30% and 40% of them 'find great difficulty in attaining a degree of independence in adult life comparable to that of young people in the general population' (Hirst & Baldwin, 1994, p110). Specifically, the study concluded that disabled young people:

● were less likely to be living independently of their parents than young people in general

● were half as likely as other young people to be in paid work

● often faced long-term dependence on the social security system, incomes substantially below those of young people in general and restricted personal spending

● often did not control the money from their social security benefits

● were more likely than their non-disabled peers to report feelings reflecting a poor sense of their own worth and abilities and a limited sense of control over their lives

● had more limited social lives, were less likely to have close friendships (including boy/girlfriends) and were more dependent on their parents for their leisure activities than their non-disabled peers.

For young people who have high levels of need for support and/or continuing health care needs, the barriers to independent adulthood are likely to be even greater than for young people generally. This is also the group for whom services are the most important; their standards of health, the quality of their lives and indeed, for some, even their life expectancy will depend on their access to health and support services.

There is still limited information on the experiences of transition to adulthood for young people with health and support needs. As Christine Eiser points out in her work on children and young people with chronic illness:

'In the past, there was little attempt to document the specific difficulties of adolescents with chronic disease, largely because of the limited life expectancy associated with many conditions which precluded the possibility of long-term survival. Thus, it has only recently been acknowledged that adolescents with chronic disease face very special difficulties in their attempts to attain independence and autonomy. Successful separation from the nuclear family, career choices, marriage and parenting are difficult for all adolescents and young adults, but especially so for those with chronic disease.' (Eiser, 1993, p71).

This group of young people are particularly in need of co-ordinated, sensitive and flexible responses to their needs on the part of health and social services organisations. A smooth transition from children's to adults' services, with assessments which focus on needs rather than on slotting people into existing services, will also make a major difference to the quality of their lives. It is clear that this does not always happen; the six local authorities consulted during this work recognised that there are major problems with transition from children's to adults' services. Indeed, various reports by joint planning/joint commissioning groups included statements such as:

'Families say it's like disappearing into a void'

'Young people feel abandoned once they reach adulthood.'

This echoes the opinion of some service providers:

'…such are the advances in treatment in many fields, such as cystic fibrosis, that their survival into adulthood is occurring. It is now generally recognised that these young adults are "hurtling into a void" of unco-ordinated or absent health services and other provision.'
(Chamberlain & Rooney, 1996 p88)

What do we know about the number of young people with 'health and support needs'?

One of the major issues identified by the six local authorities was the incomplete and confusing information about the number of young disabled people and the nature of their needs. The starting point for many national estimates of young disabled people is still the surveys of children and adults conducted in the mid-1980s by the Office of Population and Censuses and Surveys. These found that there were 340,000 young disabled people aged between 16 and 29 in Great Britain, accounting for 5% of all disabled people and 2.5% of all young people. Twenty thousand young people of this age group were living in residential establishments and men outnumbered women by 1:1.2 (Martin *et al.*, 1988).

On the basis of prevalence rates established by the OPCS survey, Anne Chamberlain states:

> 'We may expect 21 teenagers aged 16–19 years, and 29 young people aged 20–29 years per thousand of their respective age groups to have at least one disability' and 'In a health district of average size (pop. 250,000) we may expect to identify easily between 30 and 40 school leavers per year' (Chamberlain, 1993, p23).

However, national prevalence rates have been found to be of limited value in establishing local incidence rates. For example, a local study of school-leavers in the London boroughs of Lewisham and Southwark found a higher level of young people with 'moderate or severe disabilities' than that

13

indicated by prevalence rates derived from the OPCS national survey (Young Adults Transition Project, 1998a, p5). Discrepancies are likely to be due to two factors: varying definitions of 'disability' used by local sources of data, and local social, economic and environmental factors which have an impact on the incidence of specific impairments and conditions.

One of the biggest problems facing planners is that local sources of information all have varying ways of gathering data; health, social services, education and voluntary organisations tend to work with different definitions of disability and needs. In one local authority area, a joint planning group which was set up to consider transitional arrangements for young people with 'complex needs' found that their initial discussions were dominated by disagreement and misunderstandings about 'prevalence and definitions'. Progress was only possible once they suspended these discussions.

There is no nationally agreed categorisation which applies across agencies. Many health districts use the Special Needs Module[1] to compile a child health database, but the categories and definitions do not usually match those used by social services departments, whose definitions of disability derive from their statutory obligations laid down by the *Children Act 1989* and the *Chronically Sick and Disabled*

---

1 The Special Needs Module is designed to record information on children who will require services because of 'functional impairment'. There are nine 'problem' categories, and each 'problem' is rated as mild, moderate, severe or profound. The categories are: motor, manipulation/hand function, vision, hearing, communication, developmental delay/learning, persistent disability in health or growth, personal care, behavioural/emotional/personal.

Persons Act 1970. Both these pieces of legislation use the definition contained in the *National Assistance Act 1948* which, it could be argued, is both offensive and outdated:

> 'persons who are blind, deaf or dumb, or who suffer from mental disorder of any description, and other persons who are substantially and permanently handicapped by illness, injury or congenital deformity.'
> (National Assistance Act 1948, Section 29(1))

Another problem is that registers of disabled children and adults often do not allow for the identification of those with 'multiple impairments', and neither do registers of those with visual impairments. SeeAbility's research into the needs of school-leavers with visual impairment and 'additional disabilities' in the west of England concluded that:

> 'most registers do not include records of multiple-disability. In fact, people with multiple-disabilities could be registered as learning disabled, physically disabled, visually disabled, or any combination of the three.'
> (Miller, 1996, p4)

Two examples of authorities which keep registers in a way that allows the identification of those with 'multiple impairments' show that a significant number of adults and children are involved. In Cornwall, 46% of those registered with a visual impairment in 1995 had an additional physical impairment (Miller, 1996, p5), while in one of the local authorities from which information was gathered for the purposes of this report, 218 (36%) of the 609 children on their register of disabled children were registered as having more than one impairment.

Information on numbers of disabled people may also be derived from information about service provision, but will be related to eligibility criteria and the division of services into 'client groups'. There may, therefore, be statistics on numbers of people with 'severe learning disabilities', but these will merely reflect the numbers of people who have been able to access services for this group.

It is generally recognised that there is a lack of information on numbers of people with specific conditions associated with 'complex health and support needs'. For example, with regard to people with head injuries:

● National figures are out of date and do not take account of changing patterns of incidence.

● There is very little local data collection.

● There is very little co-operation and sharing of information between health and social services authorities in respect of numbers of people with head injury.

(Social Services Inspectorate, 1997b)

It is unclear how young people with conditions such as cystic fibrosis or sickle cell disorder are recorded, and the situation is further obscured by the fact that many of these conditions have associated complications. For example, people with cystic fibrosis may develop liver disease and diabetes. They may be picked up within the Special Needs Module used by health districts – in the category 'persistent disability in health or growth' – but these young people may not be seen as coming within the definition of disabled person applied by social services departments. This situation is compounded by the fact that most of these young people would not see themselves as disabled, either. Yet many of them would come under the definition of disability contained within the *National Assistance Act 1948* – ie the definition used by the *Children Act*, the *Chronically Sick and Disabled Persons Act* and other community care legislation.

One final point on the number of young people with health and support needs relates to the inadequate information we currently have about whether incidence varies according to race and gender, and, if it does, what the implications are for service provision. A study that included all those with cerebral palsy born in the Liverpool health district between 1971 and 1972 and between 1976 and 1978 found that there were twice as many boys as girls. It is not clear whether this gender imbalance was present at birth to the same extent, or whether differential death rates created the disparity by the time the study sampled the age cohorts in the late 1980s (Stevenson *et al.*, 1997, p338). Cystic fibrosis, sickle cell disorder and thalassaemia are all conditions which are correlated with ethnic origin, as are other, rarer, inherited conditions. As with gender, this is an unexplored issue in terms of the implications for service provision.

> **Do you have common definitions and ways of gathering information about young people with health and support needs, which have been agreed by all local agencies?**

Is the number of young people with 'health and support needs' increasing?

Throughout the industrialised world, there is evidence of both an increase in the number of children with significant impairments, and survival rates into adulthood (Blum, 1991). At the same time, it has been recognised that 'chronic conditions are frequently difficult to define in a unified fashion' (Blum, 1991, p101).

Nevertheless, those working in various specialist fields report increasing rates of incidence and survival. For example, there are thought to be increasing numbers of children born with cerebral palsy, and they are surviving for longer:

> 'There is now increasing evidence, not only that the life expectancy of children with severe disabilities, and with CP in particular, is greater than originally thought, but also that the prevalence of CP at birth is increasing.' (Stevenson *et al.*, 1997, p336)

With some conditions, there may not be an increased prevalence rate at birth, but improved survival rates mean an increasing number of children and young adults in the population. This is the case with cystic fibrosis, as Jean Pownceby points out:

> 'Whereas 50 years ago children almost inevitably died in infancy, the majority of affected individuals are now surviving to adulthood. Many CF centres currently report a median life expectancy of 20 to 25 years with a

predicted median for children born now of 40 years... The biggest growth is in the adult age group which presently stands at 2,100 and is expected to increase by 120 each year. It is anticipated that by the year 2000 almost half the CF population will be over 16 years of age.' (Pownceby, undated (a), p2)

The number of children with significant learning difficulties, who also often have physical and sensory impairments, seems to be increasing in early childhood, and in the next few years this will have an impact on the number making the transition to adulthood. Attention has been drawn, for example, to the increasing survival rate of premature babies and those with congenital conditions, and the consequent increase in the number of children with 'severe and profound disabilities' (Alberman et al., 1992).

Anecdotal evidence suggests that residential schools catering for children with 'multiple impairments' are experiencing an increase in the number of children who have continuing health care needs. The head teacher of one such school, interviewed during the course of this review, reported an 'increase in the number of medically vulnerable children placed here' and is of the opinion that 'this population is like a time bomb'.

She also reported an increase in referrals to the school of young people aged 14–16: 'This is when it becomes very difficult for parents to manage at home because of the amount of lifting involved.'

For some conditions, increasing incidence is associated
not with survival at birth but with survival at a later age. In
1970, 90% of those with severe head injury died. Now, most
survive and they 'are often young people on the point of
becoming independent from home' (Social Services
Inspectorate, 1997b, p3).

In the case of myalgic encephalomyelitis (ME), increasing
numbers may reflect both a true increase and greater
recognition of the condition. According to one estimate,
10% of cases occur in children and young people, which
means a total of between 15,000 and 30,000 children and
young people (Colby, 1994, p9). While people in their 30s are
most likely to get the illness, the second most common group
is young women aged 15–25: 'Increasing numbers of young
people are contracting the illness during school or college
training' (Colby, 1994, p9).

While there does seem to be an increase in the number of
people with a range of impairments and high support needs,
the growing awareness of their existence is also partly related
to greater social integration of people with lower levels of
support needs. The philosophy and practice of inclusion
means that it is less likely that people who have only physical
or sensory impairments, or 'mild to moderate' learning
difficulties will use specialist services. At the same time,
those with multiple and significant impairments are less likely
to be in institutional care and more likely to become users of
specialist but community-based services. For example, day
services for people with learning difficulties are increasingly

catering for people who have the most significant impairments and high support needs:

> 'The national picture shows that there are an increasing number of people with high support needs, including people who have non-verbal communication, who will be entering the service in the near future. As more people with learning difficulties go straight to college and jobs, day services are likely to be supporting a greater proportion of people who have high support needs.' (*Changing Days Bulletin*, August 1997)

Have you recognised that there are increasing numbers of young people:

- **with a range of impairments**

- **with conditions which are life-limiting and who require continuing health care?**

Present systems for gathering information do not focus on needs

Six local authorities were consulted during this review on how they gathered information about the needs of young people with health and support needs. It appeared that most of the information gathered did not focus on the actual needs of the young people concerned. Instead, strategies attempted to establish numbers of people who fell into various service categories (physical, sensory, learning disabilities, disabled children) or eligibility criteria (banding according to levels of dependency). Assessment forms also tended to be primarily about establishing levels of dependency according to what children/young people could not do. These levels of dependency were also clearly linked to eligibility criteria for service response.

Health professionals' assessments are often said to be more about individual needs, but in fact they are still often about measuring what a young person cannot do. For example, as Anne Chamberlain points out, the Barthel measurement of 'Activities of Daily Living' (widely used by health professionals) is 'too narrowly focused on physical function' (Chamberlain, 1993, p65). Chamberlain also argues that measurements of outcome of treatments by health care professionals should be more closely related to young people's own aims and experiences, and should include 'social integration', measured by things like number of journeys taken outside the home, work/education, independent living, leisure activities and so on:

'Improved measures must extend to assessing impact [of treatment] on young people's daily lives, their experience of well-being, and their social and economic functioning.' (Chamberlain, 1993, p66)

Young people's experiences of their impairments and their general state of health also need to be part of any outcome measure:

'Not only treatment of impairments such as spasticity and ataxia, but also the prevention of avoidable deterioration and related morbidity must be evaluated.' (Chamberlain, 1993, p66)

The same arguments could be made about assessing the impact of services purchased by social services departments. Present systems for gathering information about the performance of social services departments (including SSI inspections and Joint Reviews) are not based on measurements relating to quality of life. For example, assessments of communication needs and the provision of communication equipment will make a major difference to the lives of those with significant communication impairments. Yet there is no obligation on health or social services authorities to record or collate information on how many such assessments are done each year or how much communication equipment is provided.

Another example concerns the importance of leisure activities and friendships to young people. A number of the young people in residential care who were visited for this report said that they wanted to go out more, to see friends more, to go to the pub or the cinema. Yet there seems to be no evidence of any local authority gathering information on how often those who are in residential care go out to enjoy themselves.

A sense of the kinds of thing which make a difference to young people's lives is also gained by thinking about, for example, the implications of impairment and illness for cultural identity and the needs which therefore arise. Atkin and Ahmad's research on young people with haemo-globinopathy found that Asian young people were concerned about how thalassaemia could undermine their cultural identity. Many of the older boys, for example, bemoaned their inability to fast during Ramadan. Others complained that they could not celebrate Eid with other family members because of the demands of treatment. Some of the older young people – both boys and girls – were also unable to join in family visits to Pakistan because of the need for regular transfusions (Atkin & Ahmad, 1998, p11).

We need information systems that can monitor the extent to which concerns of this kind are addressed. Unfortunately, existing systems are often too far removed from the actual experience of young people to provide useful information.

In pursuit of better joint working between health and social services organisations, the Department of Health requires joint investment plans to be in place by 1999/2000, and local and health authorities are supposed to have gathered the joint information necessary to compile the plans in 1998/99.

The plans are intended to include a joint analysis of:

- local population needs

- current resources

- current investment

- agreed service outcomes.

The plans will then identify:

- agreed gaps in service provision

- present and future commissioning priorities.

(Department of Health, 1997, p2)

The question remains whether this will result in more being known about the needs of young people with health and support needs and whether analysis of 'agreed service outcomes' will relate to the quality of their lives.

Are you gathering information about young people's needs?

Are you measuring service outcomes in terms of what differences services make to young people's lives?

25

Part Two

What do young people with health and support needs want? What gets in the way of them getting their needs met?

This part of the report summarises what we know from existing research, and also draws on information gathered from six local authorities. Some important points are illustrated by quotations from the fourteen young people and two parents interviewed for the purposes of this report.

Information

> Like most doctors do, they used to talk over my head and to my mother.
>
> *Brian*

> I don't remember anybody talking to me about different options.
>
> *Jennifer*

Most reports on transition to adulthood for young disabled people have identified their, and their parents', needs for accessible information about entitlements and sources of support (Social Services Inspectorate, 1995a; Russell, 1996;

Ryan, 1997). Various pieces of legislation give young disabled people the right to receive information:

- The *Disability Discrimination Act 1995* requires schools, colleges and universities to provide information about how they cater for disabled students.

- The *Chronically Sick and Disabled Persons Act 1970* and the *NHS and Community Care Act 1990* require social services authorities to provide information about support services and how to get access to them.

- The *Housing Act 1996* requires housing authorities to provide information on how to get housing advice and how to get on the housing waiting list.

- The *Trade Union Reform and Employment Rights Act 1993* requires local careers services to provide information about job and training opportunities.

The Code of Practice on the Identification and Assessment of Special Educational Needs states that the Transition Plan – which must be drawn up for all young people who have a Statement of Special Educational Need – should consider 'What information does the young person need in order to make informed choices?'

Nevertheless, a lack of information is one of the key barriers identified by young disabled people. Only two of the six local authorities consulted during this research produced information aimed specifically at young disabled people, and only one produced regular, up-dated information mailed out to families of children on the Children with Disabilities Register.

Parents of young disabled people often find it difficult to get the information they need as their child grows into adulthood. One local authority reported they had been told by parents that they needed more information about services and how to get them. A Joint Commissioning Officer said: 'The information might be available but only from a variety of sources and people do not receive it as a basic right, only if they go searching for it.'

Nationally, the Family Fund Trust produces a very useful publication, *After Age 16 What Next?* (Cowen, 1996) and has just published a version aimed at young disabled people themselves (Fulford-Brown, 1999). The Council for Disabled Children has recently published *Growing Up: A guide to some information sources available to young disabled people and their families* (Beecher, 1998), but many young people and their families would also find local sources of comprehensive information helpful, particularly information on finding one's way through the maze of agencies, eligibility criteria, etc. An example of such local comprehensive information is the handbook published by aMAZE, a Brighton-based organisation (aMAZE, 1998).

One young person interviewed for the purposes of this report had a positive experience of a social worker who provided her with the information she needed. This was 22-year-old Georgina, who wanted information about her options for independent living when she left college. After she had spoken to her social worker on the telephone, 'she got back in contact with me within a day with the information I'd asked for, arranged to meet me the next week, and brought me the relevant forms. She's been brilliant.'

However, it seems more common for young people, and their families to have to draw on their own resources in order to get the information they require, as 17-year-old Charlotte – who has ME – has done through using the Internet:

'I can access information on any subject (from shopping to education) which, as I am housebound, I wouldn't otherwise be able to.'

For those who have a range of impairments, and for those who have continuing health care needs, there are specific issues about access to information. Information is a means to making choices, and if it is not received in a way which is accessible to the individual, then this impedes choice. For some young people with significant learning difficulties, information has to come in the form of experience of a number of different options, yet most of these young people are likely to be 'slotted into' existing services as they move from children's to adults' services (Social Services Inspectorate, 1996a).

Nicola Hendey's research on transition to adulthood for people with 'profound physical disabilities' found that lack of information was a key element in the lives of those in her sample who had achieved little autonomy:

'The process of obtaining information on benefits and social services provision was far more difficult for this group, as many had severe literacy and numeracy problems, on top of their physical impairments, which further socially excluded them.' (Hendey, 1998, p427).

For those who have continuing health care needs, information about the condition and treatment is a key part of becoming an adult and taking responsibility for oneself. As research on young people with a sickle cell disorder or thalassaemia found,

'A young person's understanding of their condition is a key aspect of living with a haemoglobinopathy [ie sickle cell disorder or thalassaemia]. First, understanding may directly contribute to their physical well-being in most cases; the better informed the young person is, usually the better able they are to avoid complications associated with their illness, value medical regimens and administer self care. Second, understanding is directly implicated in successful coping and can help a young person adjust to their illness. Third – and more generally – understanding informs the connotations associated with the condition.' (Atkin & Ahmad, 1998, p4)

Atkin and Ahmad found that the need for information about their condition increased as children grew into young adulthood and that

'finding out about their illness was a way of asserting their autonomy and often – especially for boys – a means of signalling their independence from their parents. Acquiring information also gave the illness meaning, independent of self, and this enabled the young person to maintain a valued self-image – a coping strategy again more common to boys' (Atkin & Ahmad, 1998, pp4–5).

If young people with health care needs generally find that information about their condition is an important part of becoming an independent adult, then this increases the importance of their autonomous relationship with medical and other professionals. It means that finding out about the condition or illness, the needs associated with it and the best way of meeting those needs, is an important part of transition to adulthood for young people with continuing health care and support needs. It is a vital part of taking responsibility for themselves and becoming clearer about who they are.

Nevertheless, almost a quarter of a sample of 104 young people with cystic fibrosis reported that they did not receive enough information from their doctors about their condition and treatment and 10% who did receive information said they didn't understand it (Pownceby, undated (b) p26). As young people are growing up they often want more information, but find that doctors continue to talk to their parents rather than to them, and/or talk in language that they don't understand. Brian reported:

'Like most doctors do, they used to talk over my head and talk to my mother. I used to pick up bits and pieces and I used to ask my mother when we came out. That was good because I didn't understand their jargon anyway. I never used to bother asking in there because I couldn't understand them. I did find out quite a bit about my condition when I was growing up, but not through the consultants, the professors. They are useless. It's all jargon. You have to ask the right people. In my case I learned a lot when I was young from the physios. No-one else ever offered us any information on it.'

A number of the young people interviewed for this report said that they wanted more information about their impairment but didn't know who to ask. As Jennifer, a 26-year-old young woman living in a residential home, communicated:

'When I was getting older I wanted to know more about my disability but there wasn't anyone to ask. I still want more information. I don't know who to ask.'

Some young people also find that the information provided by professionals is not the information they want. Georgina, for example, wanted to discuss with her consultant whether she would be physically able to carry a child and give birth, while the consultant had information only about the genetic implications of her condition:

'[She] was recently talking to me about having children and I said, "oh can I have children?" and she said "well, genetically there wasn't going to be a problem" and she went into the genetics of it. I said, "yes, I understand that but physically, you know I'm not very big, what about physically?". And she looked at me and said, "oh, I never thought of that". That was really annoying.'

The most useful sources of information are often self-help groups (such as the Association of Youth with ME, the Spinal Injuries Association and Young Arthritis Care) and people who have similar experiences. Yet none of the local authorities consulted had a strategy for ensuring that people with specific conditions in their area have access to such information.

Do you know what information young people want? Do you have a strategy for providing this information? Does the information include:

- **what young people are entitled to under relevant legislation and local policies?**

- **what services are provided by all parts of the statutory sector, ie health, education, housing, leisure and social services?**

- **what services are provided by the voluntary and private sector?**

- **details of national and local self-help and representative groups?**

Emotional support and personal development

> I took all their comments to heart and stopped
> believing in myself.
> *Charlotte*

Emotional support is a key issue for all young people in transition to adulthood. For those with high levels of support and health needs, it is arguably an even greater issue, and inadequate emotional support can be a major barrier to achieving independence and autonomy. Transition to adulthood is about personal development. While access to education and training, an income, meaningful activities, relationships and a home are important features of becoming an adult, these things are unlikely to be achieved or maintained unless the young person receives emotional support to make choices and to exert as much responsibility for themselves as their impairment or condition allows.

Parents are also often in need of emotional support during their children's transition to adulthood. Simon, aged 21 and ready to leave home, is having to cope with his father's feelings about this:

> 'I've told my father that I'm leaving home and we're
> having big rows. He thinks of me still as a child. He's
> not the sort of person you can talk to. I was closer to
> my mum [who died four years ago]. I said to him, all
> you're seeing is the chair, you're not seeing that I'm an
> independent sort of bloke. He says "well who's going

35

to care for you?" … In a way, I suppose it's frightening
for him, my mum not being here and him being here
on his own. But that's part of life, you can't do anything
about it.'

Lois, whose 18-year-old daughter recently moved into a
group home, talked about the support that parents need to
feel confident that their children will be safe. When young
people require high levels of support and/or have continuing
health care needs it can be very difficult to trust that these
needs will be met. She said:

> 'Parents have to be educated to let go. So often they
> can't let go because they're just so frightened and
> uncertain of the future. But if people were more open
> with parents all the way through I think it would be
> easier and professionals might be surprised – parents
> are over-protective because they haven't been given
> the opportunity to be anything else.'

If parents do not receive support and information to allay
their often quite understandable fears, there is a danger
that their concern will hold the young person back, rather
than support them towards independent adulthood.
As 26-year-old Michael said,

> 'The biggest barrier when I was 18 or 19 was my parents.
> I was scared they wouldn't let me go. They said stay,
> we love you. They didn't want me to leave home. They
> were really shocked that I wanted to go to college. No-
> one talked to them about how I could be independent,

they've been very alone all their lives, no-one's given them any help in that respect. It's sad. When I go home now they say, we're glad you went to college, we're glad you're now independent but it's a shame nobody talked to us about these things.'

Sources of emotional support

For most young people, their parents and their friends are the most important and the most appropriate sources of emotional support. This is no different for many young people with health and support needs. For example, research concerning young people with a sickle cell disorder or thalassaemia (Atkin & Ahmad, 1998) and research concerning those with cystic fibrosis (Pownceby, undated (a)) indicates that families are an important source of emotional support. However, services can obviously help parents, siblings and the wider family network to provide this support, as most families would benefit from some assistance with this important task.

> **Do you recognise that parents are often an important source of emotional support, and help parents to provide this support?**

Sometimes young people feel they cannot discuss their illness or condition with their parents. Atkin and Ahmad found that young people with haemoglobinopathy

> 'did not always share their experience of the illness and there are times when they hide the consequences of their condition from their parents. During these periods young people felt they have to deal with the illness on their own as well as worry about protecting their parents' (Atkin & Ahmad, 1998, p5).

Several young people interviewed in Atkin and Ahmad's study of those with sickle cell disorder or thalassaemia said that 'only those with the illness could understand what they were going through' (Atkin & Ahmad, 1998, p7).

Friendships with those who have similar experiences may be a very important source of emotional support for young people. Ironically, however, the experience of inclusive education can make it less likely that some young people will have access to this source of support. Georgina, now aged 22 and a college student, talked of how attending an ordinary comprehensive school meant that she has had little contact with other disabled people and her only contact with those who share her condition is at her annual visit to a specialist clinic. Twenty-one-year-old Ruth's contact with other young people with cystic fibrosis has also mainly been through her spells in hospital. Yet the emotional support she has gained from this contact is clear:

'When I'm admitted to hospital we sit around in a cubicle, not very big, talking about things … it's nice to have a peer group – to have a good chat with.'

Ruth also talked about the barriers that cystic fibrosis itself poses to contact with others who have the condition. The danger of cross-infection means that doctors and nurses positively discourage young people from being in close proximity to each other, yet the young people themselves insist on talking together.

> **Do you recognise the support that young people get from each other, and nurture this form of support?**

Some young people will gain support from religious or spiritual beliefs. Atkin and Ahmad's research, for example, found that Muslim young men with thalassaemia often had quite definite views about how their religion had helped them cope with their illness:

'Several, for instance, emphasised the importance of accepting one's fate. As part of this, many of these older boys described thalassaemia as a test. To this extent, the belief in Allah did not encourage despondency among young people. These young people felt that Allah would provide them with the strength and resources to cope with thalassaemia, but recognised that they were also responsible for their own care.' (Atkin & Ahmad, 1998, p23)

Doreen, who tries as a parent to promote her son's interests, was dismayed that the residential school he was at did not take her religious beliefs seriously:

> 'We're Methodists and I had asked that someone take him to church, at least once a month. But the person who was head of education said "what for, he won't understand." To me that doesn't matter, the Bible says suffer the little children to come unto me. He really opposed it but never really explained to me why he thought it wasn't going to do anything for Paul. I thought at least it would get him out of there and make him part of the community.'

Anne Chamberlain's report for the Department of Health recognised that statutory services must concern themselves with the broad aims of personal development when providing access to treatment and services. Transition services, she says, 'should provide not only full assessment but treatment and access to specialist services which will assist the younger person in the tasks of maturation' (Chamberlain, 1993, para 8).

This is recognised by the Leeds Young Adult Team, which provides a holistic service to young disabled people between the ages of 16 and 25 and has found the help they are able to give with psychological issues – such as low self-esteem, dependence on parents and low expectations – to be a very important part of their service (Chamberlain & Rooney, 1996). Giving young people confidence in themselves and increasing their self-esteem is something that all professionals in contact with them can seek to achieve.

> **Do your commissioning strategies and plans for service development include the provision of emotional support to young people and their families?**

Emotional support and health care needs

Young people can experience specific difficulties associated with their condition or impairment, and may need emotional support geared towards these experiences. For example, young people with sickle cell disorder have to deal not only with the pain when they have a crisis but also with the fear of pain: 'Their dread of the pain returning ... meant they worried about it even when they were well' (Atkin & Ahmad, 1998, p25).

Not much attention has been paid to the worries and concerns that may be the legacy of a childhood dominated by operations. If a young adult has memories of nightmarish experiences of hospitals and treatment as a child, they will be less likely to agree to further treatment. Jennifer, for example, has a fear of the oxygen mask which was put on her when she was in intensive care following an operation as a child. Sometimes, a young person's knowledge or memory of how they acquired their impairment has continuing consequences, as in Michael's case. He has a fear of being deprived of oxygen:

> 'I don't like operations. I worry about whether I would come round, whether they would give me too much oxygen or too little. That's how I became disabled in the first place, when I had pneumonia as a baby.'

41

If professionals are to involve young people like Michael and Jennifer fully in decisions about further treatment, they need to be alert to fears of this kind and seek to address them.

Sometimes a young person's experience of health care services can in itself create a need for emotional support, particularly when they feel they have been treated in a way that undermines their self-confidence and self-esteem. Charlotte found her contact with health services particularly oppressive because it took four years and ten months to get a diagnosis and, as she said,

> 'The doctors didn't believe me when I tried to tell them how ill I felt.

> 'They made me feel so small when I went to the doctor. They were so superior and it was a really degrading experience every time. They kept doing blood tests which didn't show anything. I thought I was going mad. The fact that they didn't find anything wrong meant I had to come to the conclusion that they were right and I was wrong.

> 'I took all their comments to heart and stopped believing in myself. I hated myself because I thought I was imagining everything. I became suicidal and secretly used to cut my body with razors and burn myself with hot water. I had to give myself a reason for being in such pain – although I don't think I knew it at the time.

> 'My physical health continued to deteriorate until it got to the point where I couldn't cope at all at school. I returned to the doctor and was treated for depression, which

made me worse. I then saw a psychiatrist who said that there was nothing psychologically wrong with me, but that I had ME. I was so relieved that I wasn't going mad; the self-abuse stopped instantly.'

Continuing health care needs may be perceived as getting in the way of independent adulthood for young people and, in particular, some parents of young people with continuing health care needs believe that the young person would not be able to cope with their condition if they lived independently. These are real concerns, which it is important not to dismiss as 'over-protectiveness', particularly as, for some young people, quality and consistency of treatment have implications for their life expectancy. Ruth, who has cystic fibrosis, talked of how her mother was concerned for her health when she moved in with her boyfriend.

> 'And my mum said "oh no, you're going to get poorly". But I moved in with him. I must admit I was in hospital more often than not after I moved in with him. I did do my treatment, but sometimes with physio you're coughing this horrible stuff up and you don't like doing it in front of your boyfriend.'

Some young people themselves are worried about their ability to live independently, as Nicola Hendey's research found:

> 'Many people worried about what might happen in an emergency if they were living alone, and this was of particular concern to the sample members with epilepsy who worried about injuring themselves during a fit.

Olivia's comments were typical: "I am scared of living on my own because of my illness really. Sometimes when I have bad fits I have nasty falls and hurt myself".'
(Hendey, 1998, p170)

If young people such as Ruth and Olivia are ever to have the chance of living independently, they need emotional support to help them address their health care needs. Without this support, the provision of more concrete forms of support – such as affordable and appropriate housing – will not be enough to meet their needs.

Emotional support and life-limiting or life-threatening conditions

Adolescence is a time of rebellion, and is often characterised by wanting to be different from the way the adults in a young person's life wish them to be. Young people with continuing health care needs have authoritative adults (parents, doctors, physiotherapists and other professionals) in their lives, telling them they need to take medication, have an operation, do particular exercises or have regular treatment 'for their own good'. Many young people in these situations find it difficult to comply, and for some the consequences can significantly reduce the quality of their lives and may shorten their lives. For example, although more people with thalassaemia are surviving into their twenties and thirties because of better medical understanding and treatment of the condition, 'early death through non-compliance with chelation therapy is common' (Atkin & Ahmad, 1998, p3).

Ruth eloquently describes the need to exert some kind of control in a situation where parents and professionals are insisting on compliance with treatment (for cystic fibrosis) which is time-consuming, unpleasant and not something an adolescent wishes to spend her life doing:

> 'We do know that we need it, but it's just that at that one time you think, I don't want this, it's like rebellion…I just think that sometimes you just have to not do something one day, like you need to control it. Whenever I've been on my IVs [intravenous treatment] and I've been in hospital for 14 days and I go home and the next day, I do no physio, just for one day, because it makes me feel in control.'

Similar issues are raised by research about young people treated for cancer:

> 'Adolescents may rebel against unwanted dependency through hostility or treatment refusal which might decrease their chances of long-term survival' (Roberts *et al.*, 1998, pp5–6).

This article argues that clinics should set up support groups and suggests that

> 'social work interventions with individuals, families and groups can be very valuable in helping adolescents deal with biopsychosocial issues and preventing long-term problems during survivorship' (p16).

The popular image of the experience of childhood cancer assumes that if a child survives s/he is 'cured' and resumes a 'normal' life. The after-effects of chemotherapy and surgery, and the disruption of education and relationships mean, in reality, that the consequences can be significant and long-term. Young people have been found to be at risk of isolation from their peers and of difficulties in forming sexual relationships. These experiences were related to loss of confidence because of illness and changed body image (Roberts *et al.*, 1998).

Young people with experiences of this kind may have concerns about having children, life expectancy and other issues. They are quite likely to have formed friendships with people with similar conditions who then die. They may also feel burdened by their families' feelings about their condition. Atkin and Ahmad's research found that young people with haemoglobinopathy were aware of their parents' sadness about their condition and 'this can generate a sense of guilt among young people' (Atkin & Ahmad, 1998, p14):

> 'Most young people, especially as they grow older, are especially sensitive to their parents' sadness and distress. Dealing with their parents' worries adds to the general difficulties faced by young people in coming to terms with their illness. There are times, for instance, when the young person does not know whom to turn to for support, and this undermines their ability to cope with the condition and maintain a valued sense of self.'

The six young people in Alison Closs's exploration of quality of life for children and young people with 'serious medical conditions' had all faced the possibility of early death, and five of them experienced crises in their conditions and treatment which were then followed by periods of acute anxiety and depression.

> 'For Martin and Eleanor it was the prospect of a heart and heart-lung transplant respectively, Laura was told by her consultant that further pain relief was not possible and that she would have to have neck surgery which might leave her paralysed, and Amy had to be resuscitated twice after asthma attacks. John's nurse training was terminated at the age of 18 both because of his clumsiness and the simultaneous diagnosis of his condition. "It really seemed like the end of the world. I had no future. I was just devastated. It took me years to find my way again." Even Eleanor, who hopes a transplant may be a new beginning, said, "I was shocked. Had my illness really come to this? I cried. I cried a lot over the next while".' (Closs, 1998, p115)

Are counselling and psychological support services available for young people to address issues relating to living with life-limiting and life-threatening conditions? Are resources put into setting up support groups?

However, while those seeking to support young disabled people in their transition to adulthood should be alert to the emotional support that young people might need, it is important not to make assumptions about how best to meet those needs. For example, one group of young people with cerebral palsy identified that it was their **parents** who were most in need of counselling in order to cope with disability in adolescence (Spastics Society, 1978, p14).

Sometimes, it is young people's experiences of services that create emotional difficulties for them. Michelle, for example, was one of a number of young people interviewed who were placed in residential settings where most other people were older than they were. She said:

> 'The worst thing about being here is that not only are most people very much older than me but they are also ill and that's often carried them off. People die, and despite my strong faith I can't come to terms with it – I mean, I'm not ready to die.'

It is also important to recognise that young disabled people may want emotional support with the kinds of thing which are of concern to any young person – difficulties with relation-ships, the death of a parent, problems with school or college work. Simon, for example, spoke of how he gave up college to look after his mother, who died of cancer four years ago.

People with communication impairments and/or 'challenging behaviour' may be particularly unlikely to receive emotional support. This was the experience of Barbara, who talked of how she needed support when her father died.

> 'When my dad died I wasn't allowed to grieve. Everybody wanted me to look happy. Counselling has helped me to come to terms with it all. It's still painful – last Saturday it was ten years since I lost him and all day I was in tears on and off. I thought this is silly, ten years but I was mourning like it was yesterday. But I'm talking about it more and more and that's why it's all coming out. I hate feeling sad. I still haven't really grieved properly.'

Are counselling and psychological support services available for young people, including those with communication impairments and/or 'challenging behaviour'?

Advocacy, mentoring and peer support

> It's nice to be able to talk to someone who's got the
> same thing, like if a doctor has said you need this
> and they don't really explain it.
> *Ruth*

Services also need to pay attention to the provision of
advocacy, mentoring and peer support. Unfortunately,
where these forms of support do exist they are most likely
to be developed on an *ad hoc* basis by self-help groups with
short-term and insecure funding. Only one of the six local
authorities consulted for the purpose of this report had a
policy of providing independent advocacy services to young
people in transition to adulthood. None of them had put
any resources into mentoring and peer support initiatives,
although two authorities had funded personal assistance
support schemes for people who use direct payments (and
peer support to direct payment users may have been part
of the scheme).

Advocacy and people with significant communication impairments

When young people have significant communication
impairments and/or learning difficulties, their need for
advocacy is heightened and yet also more difficult. As Tessa
Harding wrote, when she evaluated an advocacy service for
deafblind people:

'Advocacy is particularly important for deafblind people since many have such difficulty expressing their needs and wants, but also particularly difficult, since the advocate will need to make exceptional efforts to understand the wishes and preferences of their [advocate] partner.' (Harding, 1995, pp1–2)

Yet, as Harding also observes:

'It is possible to form [advocacy] partnerships in spite of communication difficulties. Advocates need to be sensitive to their partner's abilities and be willing to learn how best to communicate with them, rather than acquiring specialist communication skills … Patience, attention, empathy and sensitivity to the individual's own methods of communication, together with the will to understand, seem to be the human qualities required of advocates.' (Harding, 1995, p2)

Harding's evaluation of the Sense Advocacy project clearly illustrates the particular need that people with significant communication impairments – who are especially likely to be in institutional settings – have for an advocate. She describes one of the deafblind people whom the project helped. The woman concerned had 'very little movement and no speech, but is able to express pleasure, by smiling, and displeasure, pain or anger by biting her hand' (Harding, 1995, p3).

The woman was living on a hospital ward with twenty-three other people and only three or four staff. As Harding points out:

'In these circumstances staff are under considerable pressure and there is a real risk that respect for personal dignity and individual rights are overlooked. There is no-one other than the advocate to give this partner the time and the personal attention she needs, not just to exercise any choice in her own life, but also to provide human warmth, personal concern and affection and to accord dignity and respect. This woman responded noticeably to the attention of the advocate, gradually relaxing and becoming calm and responsive; she became tense again when the patient attention and gentle touch were withdrawn.' (Harding, 1995, p3)

Parents and siblings of people with significant communication impairments sometimes feel that they are the only consistent people in the young person's life who understand how they communicate and who can advocate for their interests. It is widely recognised that parents' views and interests may conflict with those of their children once they are young adults, yet if there is no other source of advocacy available to young people with communication impairments, parents have no choice but to attempt to represent their interests. As Lois says, who acts as an advocate for her 18-year-old daughter (who does not use speech and has significant learning difficulties), 'Professionals come and go and it's only the parent who is the constant'.

Yasmin, who lives in a residential home, has complex feelings about her parents and feels she needs help to assert her independence from them: 'I feel very close to my parents. They are still my parents,' she said, and yet 'I feel as if all I ever do is say yes and no to my parents. I can't tell them what I really feel. The point I want to make to them is that I want to be independent. My sister-in-law backs me up and says let Yasmin live her life'.

> **Do you have a strategy for providing advocacy services for young people, including those with significant communication impairments?**

Peer support and mentoring

All young people value the support of their peers and the encouragement of people older than them whom they admire and whose example they want to emulate. Such sources of support can be particularly important for young people who have health and support needs. The uncertainties of adolescence can be made much worse when a young person has little or no contact with adults who have the same kinds of support need as they do. Barbara spoke of how

> 'when I thought about my future, I thought I would be in a home because I didn't have a lot of confidence in myself. I remember one day we had to write an essay about where would you be in ten years' time. I put on my essay how do I know that? And I got an F! My two friends put the same. I thought I would be in a home all my life but I'm not.'

People who have specific health care needs often find that the best support comes from others with the same condition. The value of peer support and mentoring by people with similar experiences is demonstrated by Young Arthritis Care Positive Futures workshops. Young people who went on one of these residential weekend workshops for teenagers with arthritis reported how important it was to meet other people of their age with similar experiences:

> 'The most important part of the weekend was meeting other people with arthritis that were my age. It made me realise that I am not the only young person with arthritis. It has made me look at my life differently and made me realise I can still do the things I have always dreamed of.'
> (*Information Sheet for Teenagers*, Positive Future Workshops)

And another young person said: 'Weekends like this are really good because when you're having a bad day you can remember that you are not alone.'

Young Arthritis Care has been running these residential workshops for some time now. Over the course of a weekend participants discuss:

- What does arthritis mean to me?
- How am I affected – in school, social life, travel, getting around?
- What stops us doing what others do?
- How I feel about myself; how others treat me – friends, family, the media, charities.

- How to speak up for myself – being more confident.

- Relationships with other children/teenagers, family and the doctor.

- Future plans – what are my goals?

Volunteers provide personal assistance throughout the weekend so that young people do not have to bring their parents with them to provide any help they need.

In order to promote peer support, specific barriers created by the long-term condition often have to be overcome. For example, the risks of cross-infection can inhibit face-to-face contact between people with cystic fibrosis, and low energy levels can prevent people with ME from getting together. Organisations are, however, finding ways around these barriers, using teleconferencing, emails, newsletters and videos. The Association of Youth with ME, for example, videos its annual conferences and sends copies to those who cannot attend. Seventeen-year-old Charlotte pays tribute to the difference that AYME has made to her life:

> 'AYME has played a very important part in my life. As well as giving me practical advice and support, through it I have become friends with many other young people in the same position as me, which has stopped me from feeling so isolated. Although I have not been strong enough to meet them in person, we keep in contact by letter or telephone on our better days. AYME has given me back my self-confidence by allowing me to work for them whenever I am well enough.'

Peer support, mentoring and 'treatment compliance'

With some conditions, treatment, medication and/or surgery can make a major difference to the quality of life and life expectancy. 'Treatment compliance' is identified by many professionals as a difficult area during adolescence, and some young people experience long-term consequences as a result. Contact with others with the same condition, particularly with those who are older, may often be the most effective way of helping young people to accept necessary treatment. Atkin and Ahmad's research on young people with thalassaemia found that non-compliance with chelation therapy was particularly high between the ages of 13 and 17 but, as the consequences became evident, 'all those young people who had not used their infusion pump regularly now regretted their decision and hoped that others would not make the same mistake' (Atkin & Ahmad, 1998, p9).

Young people who have experienced the consequences of not taking medication or treatment are an under-used resource for supporting young people who are still struggling with this stage in their lives.

This is also an issue identified by those working with adolescents who have cancer. Arguing that services should set up peer support groups, Roberts *et al.* point to evidence that:

> 'Teens who are resentful about what they perceive to be parental interference or overprotectiveness (eg limiting social activities when resistance to infection is low) can

be challenged in their thinking by other teens who point out the need for precautions to maintain health.'
(Roberts *et al.*, 1998, p15)

According to the Long-term Medical Conditions Alliance (LMCA), there are 85 voluntary organisations representing and made up of people who have a long-term illness. People who live with a long-term condition become expert on their needs; their expertise is an important resource in the management of their condition and in supporting each other. Recognising this, the LMCA has initiated a Living with Long-term Illness project that aims to work with ten organisations, such as Arthritis Care, to develop self-management models of care.

Do you draw on the expertise of individuals with health and support needs, and voluntary organisations representing them, to provide advocacy, mentoring and peer support?

Education

> I think the trouble with my schooling was that they
> didn't give me the support I needed.
> *Michael*

> They found my complex problem an inconvenience.
> *Charlotte*

Some of the young people included within the category
of 'complex health and support needs' are those children
most likely to experience segregated education. In particular,
children and young people with 'multiple impairments' will
usually attend a special school rather than receive their
education in a mainstream school. For example, an RNIB
survey published in 1992 found that:

> 'Visually impaired children fall into two distinct groups:
> those with and those without other disabilities. Those
> with the most severe visual impairments and with the
> most additional impairments tend to be at special
> schools.' (quoted in Miller, 1996, p10)

Children and young people with a range of impairments
are also more likely to attend residential schools and, if
they receive further education (which many of them do
not, according to the Further Education Funding Council),
to attend a residential college.

Education for independent living?

At the point at which young people with health and support needs are making the transition to adulthood, many of them are also faced with the consequences of interrupted or poor quality education. One young man interviewed as part of a study on disabled people's experiences of higher education talked of how his years at a special school led to educational disadvantage:

> 'There were some good points about being there, like having our own swimming pool and good days out. But mostly I didn't really enjoy school because the standard of education was so poor and we were never pushed, academically, in class. There were big differences in intelligence levels within each class, the teachers had to teach everyone and couldn't cater for anyone individually, so we spent most of our time playing. I never had the chance to take any exams or get any qualifications while at school.' (Bennett, 1997, p32)

This type of experience is reflected in some of the accounts by the young people interviewed for this report. Some felt their abilities were unfairly judged. As Michael, now aged 26 and living in a residential setting, said:

> 'It's quite sad, really, that when I left there, because my schooling wasn't so marvellous I was told I had a mental age of six. That's what they told me when I left at the age of 18. I don't know what they expected of me, I thought I had tried my very hardest. After being there for years and

trying my very hardest, for someone to say just
before you leave that you've got a mental age of six,
it's very disheartening. I was very upset that someone
had said, oh you've got a mental age of six. I thought
what's the point?'

A small-scale piece of research carried out by a teacher,
Denise Dew-Hughes, looked at the comparative experiences
of two groups of children, one at a special school, the other
at a mainstream school, all of whom had 'severe learning
disabilities'. She found that the children in the special
school received fewer hours of teaching, were given little
responsibility for their own belongings or equipment or
opportunities to choose their activities, and seemed less
mature and more dependent on adult help (*Times Educational
Supplement*, 14 March 1997).

Nicola Hendey's research on young people with physical
impairments who need personal assistance in their daily
lives illustrates the dissatisfaction that many young disabled
people have with the education system:

'The majority of the sample had, during their school
years, high expectations with regard to their own ability
and many had expressed a willingness to sit some
examinations. On leaving school the majority had never
been entered for any examinations and many were
lacking basic literacy and numeracy skills and this was
a source of considerable distress and embarrassment
to them and further hampered an uncertain future.'
(Hendey, 1998, p161)

Unequal access

Some young people have quite clearly been denied access to appropriate education because of a failure of schools to meet their needs. Simon and Georgina have similar impairments and access needs, yet their experiences of education could not be more different. While Georgina's parents were successful in their fight for their daughter to attend a mainstream comprehensive school (even though there was no lift in the school and Georgina needed personal assistance during the day), Simon's education opportunities were severely curtailed from the age of 14 when the upper school to which he should have transferred said they couldn't take him because there was no lift in the school:

> 'When I was 14, all my age group left to go to the high school and I stayed down in the middle school. The high school was all upstairs except for one course on performing arts that I went to but I didn't get on with it. All the English and maths GCSEs were upstairs and so I didn't do that. They offered me and this other boy in a wheelchair an RSA course. The middle school could only cater for RSA so that's what we did.'

These experiences of unequal access to inclusive education are confirmed by research which found that, while the proportion of pupils with a statement of special educational need attending mainstream schools is increasing, so too are the differences between local education authorities (Sebba, 1997). In the London Borough of Newham, 89% of pupils with statements are in mainstream schools, while in Coventry only 29% are (Centre for Studies on Inclusive Education, 1998).

Children and young people who have communication impairments are sometimes denied access to education because their communication needs are not properly addressed. Susan, who doesn't use speech, communicated that:

> 'My biggest ambition when I was 18 was to have a Liberator Talker. I only had a book to communicate with. I found out about Liberator Talkers when I was 18 and I was at a residential college. The first one I had was a small one and it wasn't very good for me. My aunt paid for it.'

Hendey also found examples of young people who did not receive appropriate communication equipment when they were younger. One person said: 'I didn't get my touch talker until I was 16, so I couldn't communicate until that time. I had to use my body to talk. I couldn't do lessons' (Hendey, 1998, p304).

Children and young people whose conditions mean that they have difficulty attending school, such as those with ME, should receive home tuition. Government guidance states that: 'Children should not be left at home without tuition for more than four weeks' (Department for Education, Department of Health and NHS Executive, 1994, p4). Nevertheless, it appears possible for such children to drop through the net; Charlotte, aged 17 and who has ME, has not received any education since the age of 14. She said:

'When I became too ill to attend school at all, my parents officially withdrew me. [The school] had no further contact with me. When I first left school, at 14, I did consider home tuition and we saw someone from the Pupil Support and Special Educational Needs Service. They offered me several hours of home tuition a week, but I became too ill. No-one has been in contact with me since.'

Education and treatment

Some young people's need for physiotherapy gets in the way of access to education. The interruption of lessons to attend physiotherapy is something that many adults who attended special schools complain about. Those in Hendey's sample who attended segregated schools echo the experiences of many. They reported 'great difficulty due to physiotherapy interrupting their lessons'. For all of them, physiotherapy ceased once they left school, and only three out of forty-two people felt that physio had helped them. As one young person said:

'I missed out on a lot of education through having physio. I had too much physio all day long. As soon as I went into school in the morning I had to go straight into the physio room. You would have physio for an hour or so and then go back to your class. A few hours later you would be called back to physio ... I had no schooling!' (Hendey, 1998, p293)

In contrast, Georgina – who attended a mainstream school – went to physio after school.

Hospital treatment can also impede access to education. One study of young people with arthritis highlighted the consequences of time spent in hospital.

'For those children who are hospitalised for long periods of time, the amount of education they received is vital for their future. Very few hospitals still have full-time schools and the minimum education requirement of three hours per week is derisory. … A majority of young adults who had arthritis as childen complained of insufficient liaison between school and hospital.' (Leak, 1994, pp885–6)

Even when young people do receive teaching in hospital, they may find that it is not at the appropriate level. Ruth complained that, when she was doing her GCSEs, the hospital she was in didn't understand

'how important it was for me to keep up with my school work … I think the hospital teachers sometimes treat us as stupid, they just do basic English and maths.'

The National Curriculum is not mandatory in hospital schools, although guidance says that 'hospital teachers should try to provide a broad and balanced curriculum complementary and comparable to that in mainstream school' (Department for Education, Department of Health and NHS Executive, 1994, p3).

Attitudinal barriers

Atkin and Ahmad's research found that some young people with haemoglobinopathy felt that teachers had 'written off' their chances of academic success (Atkin & Ahmad, 1998, p32). Many disabled adults testify to the lack of self-confidence that has followed what they believed to be negative attitudes by teaching staff, in mainstream and in special schools. One young person said:

> 'They said I was thick at school because if somebody doesn't teach you to read and write you do look thick to the average person. They just left me in a corner with a paintbrush and some paints. People used to ask me to read something and when I couldn't they just used to stand back.' (Hendey, 1998, p303)

Young people have also identified problems with the attitudes of careers advisors. Atkin and Ahmad found that:

> 'Few young people had received "helpful" career advice at school. Careers advisors did not seem well informed about haemoglobinopathies and, more generally, young people did not see career advice as helpful in deciding what their career options were.'

The research also found that racism played a part in the attitudinal barriers experienced by these young people:

> 'In some cases the involvement of the careers advisor was especially negative. Several young people

commented that the careers advisor had especially low expectations of their ability, based more on ethnic stereotypes than on assumptions about their condition.' (Atkin & Ahmad, 1998, p33)

Georgina talked about the negative attitude of the careers advisor that she saw:

'When I was about 16 I wanted to teach. I spoke to the careers adviser specifically for people with disabilities. He was really dismissive and said maybe I could teach in a special school because there was no way I would be able to teach in mainstream.'

Access to further and higher education

It is generally agreed that further education opportunities for young disabled people have improved in recent years, but that young people who have high levels of need for support are still often denied access to further education (Angele *et al.*, 1996). Those who need a lot of personal assistance or who have significant learning difficulties often finish their full-time education at the age of 19. It was noticeable that a number of the young people interviewed for this report felt that they had been almost forced out of education at the age of 19. As Robert put it, 'it was strange leaving school, worrying. They said to me, why can't I go quicker, they said they wanted to get rid of me, quick.' Although he said he thought 'they were joking', he still felt rejected, as did Louise, who reported that, when she reached the age of 19, 'they basically said there was no more they could do for me. I said "surely there's more you can do for me?"'

If young people with high levels of support needs do continue in further education, it is likely to be at one of the specialist residential colleges, which have been criticised for focusing more on the provision of 'care' than on the development of knowledge, abilities and skills. There has also been criticism of some 'independent living skills' courses, in that they tend to focus on young people physically doing things for themselves (which for many may be unrealistic or take up too much time) rather than encouraging 'independence of mind'. As Michelle said:

> 'They tried to get me to do things like dress myself, make a cup of tea … I don't know whether the college were giving me unrealistic goals. I can now partly dress myself but I would never be able to completely dress myself. Independence to me is all sorts of things, not just physical things.'

One service manager, interviewed for this review, runs a 'transition to independent living' residential service and spoke of how some young people leave special schools and further education colleges with very little ability to make choices for themselves. She was concerned that some so-called 'independent living skills courses' failed to prepare young people for living outside a residential environment:

> 'They come to us unable to take emotional responsibility for themselves, unable to take responsibility for their medication or care and unable to take financial responsibility. They're 21 going on 12.'

Moreover, some have very poor literacy and numeracy skills and this is not always because of cognitive impairment.

At a national level, the Tomlinson Committee raised concerns that provision for disabled students in colleges rarely featured in strategic planning or quality assurance mechanisms:

'Few questions are asked about the purpose or relevance of what students with learning difficulties and/or disabilities are being asked to learn. Monitoring and evaluation of students' achievements is less common in this work than elsewhere and managers often lack awareness or understanding of what is required.'
(Further Education Funding Council, 1996, p6)

Some of those who attend such colleges find that the support they need is not available. Susan said that:

'Generally the lack of facilities was a big problem [at college]. I could have done a lot more. Many times I could not put forward my ideas, opinions or feelings because there was not enough help with my [communication] board.'

In the early 1990s, a campaign, CHALLENGE, was launched by eight national disability organisations on behalf of 'young people and adults with a sensory impairment and severe learning disabilities who may have additional disabilities and challenging behaviour'. One of the aims of the campaign was to extend the statutory entitlement to education to at least age 25 for this group. Unfortunately, the campaign ceased without achieving its aims. Many young people who have experienced segregated education, especially if they then enter residential care, take a while before they are in a position to pursue further education opportunities. This was Louise's experience:

'I started a part-time course but then I got ill. It was a couple of years before I went back and started the full-time course I'm doing now, because I had to motivate myself. I had to make up my mind that that was what I wanted to do. I was ill with depression for a while. So it took me a while to motivate myself. There wasn't really anyone helping me motivate myself. It was just me making decisions and putting myself back together.'

Most of those interviewed for the purposes of this report who were living in residential care expressed an interest in further learning. Brian was fairly typical:

'I'm hoping to do more on computers. Brush up on it a bit and learn Windows 95 or whatever it is. I want to learn to get on the Internet. This will be good as it will mean that I don't have to always go out to get the information I need.'

Children and young people with a wide range of impairments and conditions have a common vulnerability to poor-quality and inadequate education. It is not their impairments or conditions that create these experiences, but the failure of schools and colleges to facilitate equal access to education.

Nevertheless, there is an increasing understanding of the nature of the barriers faced by these young people. For example, the Tomlinson Committee, which made recommendations about further education and disabled people, argued:

> 'We want to avoid a viewpoint which locates the difficulty or deficit with the student and focus instead on the capacity of the educational institution to understand and respond to the individual learner's requirement ... There is a world of difference between, on the one hand, offering courses of education and training and then giving some students who have learning difficulties some additional human or physical aids to gain access to those courses and, on the other hand, re-designing the very processes of learning, assessment and organisation so as to fit the objectives and learning styles of the students ... only the second philosophy can claim to be inclusive, to have as its central purpose the opening of opportunity to those whose disability means that they learn differently from others.' (Further Education Funding Council, 1996, p4)

For people who have continuing health needs and/or high support needs, access to education will also depend on these needs being addressed in a way which enables them to take advantage of inclusive learning. This often involves provision or funding by more than one agency. Georgina, for example, was only able to go to art college because her social services department responded to her individual needs for personal assistance and the college's accommodation for students was able to meet her needs. Similarly, research on education opportunities for adults with learning difficulties found that close collaboration between education, health, social services and voluntary/private sector agencies was an essential part of developing provision for people with the most complex learning needs (Sutcliffe & Jacobsen, 1998). This was particularly the case when people needed support workers to accompany them.

> **Do your joint commissioning strategies and mechanisms include the provision of education within their remit, and involve education agencies?**
>
> **Does transition planning for young people include continuing access to education?**

Accommodation and support

> I can't stay [living with my father] forever and I've got
> my own life to lead and I want to get on with it. I'm 21
> now and time's ticking on.
> *Simon*

> I have one main aim and that's to live in a flat of
> my own. That's all I can think about at the moment.
> *Michael*

Getting a home of your own is very difficult for most young
people, mainly because the cost of buying or renting and
running a home is difficult for anyone in the early stages of
adult life when income is likely to be low. For young disabled
people the barriers are even greater; they are less likely to be
in employment than their non-disabled peers, and the private
rented sector, the most important source of housing for the
young, has little suitable to offer. There are also the less
tangible barriers of low self-esteem and lack of confidence
that can be a legacy of a childhood spent in specialist
provision and/or living with a chronic condition. Barbara
illustrates this when she says:

> 'They told me I was ready to move out into the
> community but I wasn't. They put me in a hostel. I'd
> never been on my own at night and they left me and I
> screamed all night long. I hadn't realised there wouldn't
> be anyone there at night and it was a shock to me.'

The likelihood that young people with high levels of health and support needs will access appropriate accommodation and support, and thus achieve independent living, depends very much on whether housing and social services authorities recognise the nature of their needs and respond appropriately. This recognition needs to happen at both planning and strategic levels and as part of a response to individual requirements. Unfortunately, Simon's experience is all too common:

> 'I approached the social worker last year saying I wanted to move out and she put my name down on the housing list. I've been on the housing list for a year now and I haven't heard anything.'

Housing and social services legislation promotes the recognition of the needs of this group of young people, but in practice this statutory framework often seems not to be enough. Almost 30 years ago, the *Chronically Sick and Disabled Persons Act 1970* required housing authorities to 'have regard to the special needs of chronically sick or disabled persons'. The *Housing Act 1996* and accompanying Code of Guidance give people the right to expect help with housing in certain situations, and many young people with health and support needs should qualify for help with their housing needs. This is not just about recognising that some young people will need wheelchair-accessible accommodation, or working with housing associations and care providers to develop supported housing for people with learning difficulties. It is also about recognising that some young people will need an extra room for kidney dialysis, that someone with severe asthma needs good quality ground floor accommodation, and so on.

> **What arrangements are there to ensure that the housing requirements of young people with health and support needs are addressed in the drawing-up of local housing strategies?**
>
> **Do allocation policies give full recognition to the needs and circumstances of young people with health and support needs?**

For most of these young people, the provision of accommodation will not be the only thing they need if they are to live independently. They will need in addition some form of support, whether co-ordination of services, ongoing personal assistance or initial assistance to ensure that their health care needs are addressed once they are living away from their parents or a residential setting. While these young people's needs are the same as everyone else's – in the sense of needing to live in their own home and participate in their local community – they require support that addresses their particular experiences of their impairment or condition.

Evaluation of a project supporting people with acquired brain injury to live in their own homes illustrates this point. The following were found to be important features of the service, making it possible for people with this particular impairment to live independently with the support they needed:

- expert knowledge and experience of brain injury

- specialist support for people whom some agencies regarded as 'problematic'

- an understanding of the difficulties experienced by brain-injured people in using services

- the co-ordination of a myriad of services across people's lives

- the ability, as a non-statutory agency, to offer more effective advocacy and a truly person-centred approach

- the promotion of re-engagement with ordinary living and communities.

(Cunningham *et al.*, 1998)

The statutory framework underpinning social services departments' responsibilities for young people with health and support needs includes the *Chronically Sick and Disabled Persons Act 1970*, the *Disabled Persons Act 1986* and the *NHS and Community Care Act 1990*. Anyone who comes under the legal definition of 'disabled person' or who 'appears to be in need of community care services' has an entitlement to an assessment of their needs. Social services departments are also required to be involved in the 14+ reviews of disabled children who have statements of special educational need in their Transition Plan. The statutory framework is therefore in place which should ensure that accommodation and support needs are properly considered at an early stage in young people's transition to adulthood.

Nevertheless, young people with 'multiple impairments', especially those who require high levels of personal assistance and those who have learning difficulties and/or communication impairments, are particularly likely to move into residential care when they reach adulthood. It is sometimes difficult to disentangle the reasons for this, because they are many and complex. From Matthew's point of view, he wanted to move to the Home where he now lives: 'I chose to come to live here. I asked my social worker. He was a good social worker. I asked him if I could come and live here to be with friends.'

On the other hand, this was not how Jennifer experienced her move into residential care. Her social worker merely gave her parents a list of residential homes and did not carry out an individual assessment of her needs[1].

> Jennifer: 'I left residential school when I was 19. Before I left there was a case conference but all that was said was that there was no more they could do for me because I was now 19. I went back home to my parents.'
>
> Jennifer's Mum: 'We had social services contact from this end and they gave us a list of possible residential homes. It was a case of, well when you've found somewhere appropriate, somewhere that would accept Jennifer, then they would see whether it was viable.'
>
> Jennifer: 'I didn't want to leave home.'

---

1 Jennifer does not use speech and her mother facilitated the first meeting with her. This part of her account of her experience includes her mother's contribution.

Jennifer's Mum: 'There wasn't any option really. We were both working, her father and I. There was no way that we would be able to cope with Jennifer's needs.'

Jennifer: 'I don't remember anybody talking to me about different options.'

Other factors which make it more likely that people with high support needs will face very few options other than some form of residential care include:

- A dearth of good quality services in community settings for people who have high support needs, and particularly for those identified as having 'challenging behaviour'. Values into Action found that health and social services purchasers said that many care providers did not have the right philosophy or adequate management to provide a good quality service to those with high support needs (Ryan, 1998, p30).

- Shortage of wheelchair-accessible housing is still a major barrier to independent living for those with mobility impairments (Esmond & Stewart, 1996). Like many young people who are living in settings that are intended to be about 'transition' to independent living, Michael has found that there is nowhere suitable for him to move on to. His only hope seems to lie in the organisation's plans to build flats themselves for the young people who want to move on. 'We're hopeful, fingers crossed, that they're going to build 16 flats in what used to be a car park for this place', he said, 'and I hope to live in one of the flats with my partner who I'm living with here.'

- The cost of providing the high levels of support that some young people need can mean that health and social services purchasers will look for 'economies of scale' and are reluctant to consider even small-scale group homes.

- While there has been progress in the provision of supported living projects for people with learning difficulties – enabling them to live in 'ordinary houses' in the community – these initiatives often do not cater for people who also have mobility impairments and/or health care needs.

A number of the young people who were interviewed for the purposes of this report are effectively being 'warehoused' in residential provision; they have little opportunity to make friends, be involved in their local community or do anything meaningful during the day. To a large extent, the scope for any personal development has ceased. Jennifer, who does not use speech, communicated a number of things which indicated her lack of opportunities:

'I only keep in touch with one friend from school.'

'I'm not really happy with what I'm doing here.'

'I want to go out more.'

Michelle talked about how the inadequate support levels available are making her impairment worse:

'The short-staffing here makes my bladder problems worse and I can't always get the help at the time when I need it. They do their best, but they say "we'll come when we can".'

She also spoke of how she feels she is stagnating:

'I haven't thought about this before but I feel – I know you're always supposed to be learning things – but I feel I've been on a training course for life and I'd rather be living it. Where I am now, I feel that I'm back to where I was before I left [my parents'] home, not a lot has changed.'

These situations are most likely to continue when regular reviews of placements do not occur, or, if they do, do not assess the extent of the young person's opportunities for personal development and choice in their life. Some of the young people placed in residential establishments have little or no continuing contact with their social services department. This concern has been recognised by some professionals involved in transition planning. In one local study:

'Professionals felt there was a need to monitor outcomes of the planning process for young people and it was pointed out that there was a lack of follow-up on implementation after the young person left school.'
(Young Adults Transition Project, 1998b)

> **Is there a local commissioning strategy to enable young people with health and support needs to live 'ordinary lives' in their local communities?**
>
> **Do mechanisms for monitoring services, and reviews of individual placements, measure the extent to which young people can live 'ordinary lives' in their local communities?**

Independent living and people with significant learning difficulties and/or communication impairments

The model of independent living developed by the disability movement is based on the idea that the person who needs personal assistance is responsible for choosing who provides that assistance and directs the support they need. It is often thought that this model cannot be applied to people with significant learning difficulties, particularly those with high levels of communication needs. Yet their need (and their human right) for choices in their lives is as great as anyone's, and in recent years it has been argued that there is scope for service providers to make this possible. Research carried out by Values into Action demonstrated that it is possible for people with learning difficulties to use direct payments and also to achieve greater control over the support they need by using trusts and service brokerage (Holman & Collins, 1997; Holman & Collins, 1998).

Helen Sanderson's account of 'person-centred planning' also illustrates that it is possible for 'people with profound and multiple disabilities' to communicate their preferences and make choices about the way the support they require is delivered (Sanderson, 1998). There are exciting and empowering initiatives in existence, which are truly helping people with high levels of need to access their human rights but, as there is evidence that many young people are still being denied any choices in their lives, it would seem that there is not enough awareness of how services need to be changed in order to bring this about.

Accommodation and support and health care needs

Some young people with health and support needs require services that are knowledgeable about and sensitive to issues relating to their particular impairments. One service provider interviewed talked of how important it was for those working with, for example, a young man with brain injury, who also had sickle cell anaemia, to understand the consequences of these two conditions: 'If they don't know how to recognise and respond to his needs, his life expectancy will be shortened.'

When young people have deteriorating conditions and/or have needs which are classified as 'nursing care', the accommodation and support options open to them may be limited. For example, the head teacher at a school catering for children aged 8–19 who have 'profound and multiple learning difficulties with complex medical needs, degenerative conditions and additional sensory impairment' reported that when young people leave the school, at the age of 19, the expectation is that they will go into long-term nursing home care. These are young people who have significant communication impairments, often need high levels of support with eating and drinking, and may depend on technology such as gastrostomies and ventilators for their survival.

Not only are these young people's options limited, but their transition from residential school to nursing homes is often abrupt and badly planned. The head teacher talked of her concern at the lack of preparation experienced by the young people. There can be delays in agreement about funding for a nursing home placement which mean that the weeks and, ideally, months of preparation for moving cannot happen.

Two good practice examples were given where the staff from the nursing home to which the young person was to be transferred came to the school to observe, staff from the school went to the nursing home, the young person visited the new placement over a period of weeks, and contact was maintained with the school staff and peer group after the young person had moved. These were said to be exceptions, however.

In conversations with various professionals during the course of this review, we found a general assumption that young people with high levels of nursing care needs would have to live in nursing homes. There are a few examples of **children** being supported to live at home when the cost implications are very high. One 12-year-old girl has been supported to live at home with her family by her health authority at an annual cost of £200,000 (*Independent*, 27.8.1996, Section 2, p8). An adult with the same care needs seems to be much more likely to have to live in a nursing home. Most continuing care policies (which health authorities are required to develop) are geared towards elderly people and hospital discharge (Department of Health, 1997). In the six areas about which information was gathered for this review, in only one case did the health authority's continuing care policy mention young people with continuing nursing care needs.

When trying to find somewhere for her daughter to move on to following residential school, Lois found that a local housing and support service was initially concerned about whether they could cater for her health needs, which were likely to increase. As it turned out, her own willingness to get involved in ensuring that Phillipa's future needs were met was vital to securing her a place in a local, flexible, community-based service:

'They were seriously concerned about whether they could meet her needs, particularly her health needs. They were worried about whether in a year or two she would need nursing care that they couldn't provide. They were worried that they would need more support from the health authority and that they might have difficulty getting that. I remember saying to them at one point that it wouldn't be them that would be fighting for that, it would be me that would be noticing that Phillipa's needs were changing and getting in straight away to fight for that. I think once they realised that I was more than willing to work in partnership with them if Phillipa's needs did become more complex, that eased things a bit.'

Slipping through the net

Some young people who have health and support needs have very little or no contact with social services departments during their transition to adulthood. This can mean that they do not get the support they are entitled to and which is sometimes vital if they are to have a chance of living independently. Young people who see their condition as primarily a medical issue tend to have little contact with social services. Atkin and Ahmad found this to be the case for their sample of young people with sickle cell disorder or thalassaemia. They comment that, when contact did occur it 'was usually negative and young people commented on the ignorance of social workers' (Atkin & Ahmad, 1998, p31).

The general public seems more likely to associate social workers with child protection issues than with their statutory duties towards disabled people, and this can mean that young people and their families do not think of social services departments as a possible source of help. As Charlotte, who has ME, said, 'I've had no contact from social services. No-one's suggested they could help.'

She also went on to say that families of children and young people with ME might have particular reasons for not contacting their social services department:

'However, I don't think I would ever ask social services for any help as there are still so many cases where they have been unsympathetic towards ME sufferers. I know of several families where the sufferer has been placed on the at-risk register as social services have claimed s/he must be being neglected.'

Nevertheless, the fact is that many young people with conditions such as ME, haemoglobinopathy and so on are entitled under existing legislation to assistance with their daily lives.

Sometimes the fact that health care needs and health services are to the fore can make invisible people's social care needs and their entitlements to these forms of support. This is the experience of some young people with head injuries:

'Many people with significant head injury had had no contact with social services, either because the health services took responsibility for any continuing health care needs, or because their social care needs were never identified.' (Social Services Inspectorate, 1997, p13)

This Social Services Inspectorate report also found that:

'Many [head injury] survivors with "hidden" disabilities will fail to access mainstream local authority services as they will not meet the eligibility criteria for services for mentally ill people, or for those with physical or learning disabilities – and indeed, these services will not usually be appropriate.' (Social Services Inspectorate, 1997b, p10)

This report went on to say:

> 'Head injured people were subsumed within one of
> the major client groups (usually physical disability –
> a category suitable for only a very small proportion
> of head injury survivors). Many were excluded by the
> eligibility criteria for the larger client group, or, when
> they did access services, found them inappropriate.
> One worker commented that, because it had not been
> made clear which specialism should have the main
> responsibility for providing a service to head injured
> people, each service area was able to duck the
> responsibility.' (Social Services Inspectorate, 1997b, p14)

Young adults make up the largest group of people with head
injuries, and it is therefore especially important that transition
to adulthood services address their particular experiences
and requirements. However, their experiences of being
invisible, as far as social services departments' traditional
approaches and divisions of responsibility are concerned,
are shared by a number of young people who do not fall
easily into the categories of 'physical and sensory disability',
'learning disabilities' or 'mental health'. The importance of
this issue was highlighted by a South London Young Adults
Transition Project, which found that over a quarter of the
students in its study were only included on the basis of
a 'persistent disability in health or growth' (Young Adults
Transition Project, 1998a). This same project also found that
only 28% of school-leavers identified as 'disabled' appeared
on the central records of all three agencies, health, social

services and education. Moreover, over a third of the school-leavers identified as having 'moderate or severe disabilities' did not have statements of special educational needs.

> **Do commissioning strategies address the particular accommodation and support needs of people with 'multiple impairments' and those with continuing health care needs who do not fall within any of the traditional service headings?**

The importance of joint planning and joint working

Joint working across specialisms within social services departments is essential if people's individual needs are to be addressed, and so is joint working across health, social services, housing and education. As the Social Services Inspectorate has pointed out:

> 'Collaboration between agencies is crucial in developing systems which will enable joint planning that is flexible enough to cater for individuals and families, rather than whole client groups. This will mean individual joint planning agreements – involving health, social services, housing and education departments, the Further Education Funding Council, and employment services – may well require co-ordinated efforts over several years.' (Social Services Inspectorate, 1997b, p15)

One local authority looked at by the Social Services Inspectorate was developing 'an inter-agency commissioning strategy for people with complex service needs'. This included people with a range of conditions and was based on an acknowledgement that while 'each group has specific needs which change over time, ... at any given time, individuals across the groups may benefit from a similar service' (Social Services Inspectorate, 1997b, p16).

All people with complex needs would benefit if commissioning and service provision were multi-disciplinary, integrated and user/needs-led.

One of the consequences of a failure to establish agreed procedures for the funding of complex and often expensive 'packages' is that each person is treated as a 'one-off'. This can mean uncertainties about responsibilities, delays in making decisions and a failure to build up experience and expertise in the best ways of responding to complex health and support needs. Young people who attend specialist health clinics, such as clinics for people with cystic fibrosis, often find they do not have social work support as part of their service. Such clinics may have poor links with social services departments because:

● they are regional centres and it is difficult to build up good working relationships with a number of SSDs covering a wide geographical area

● social services departments have eligibility criteria and the groups of people they are working with do not easily fit these criteria

- health-based professionals do not have a good understanding of social services responsibilities.

The consequences of a failure to work jointly across agencies are often significant for young people, who experience fragmentation of responses to their needs, delays or failure in getting access to different services, and generally a reduction in their chances of living independently.

What arrangements are there for joint commissioning of housing and support services for young people with health and support needs?

Health

> Sometimes you need to talk about your health needs because if you don't start at the bottom of the ladder then there's no point attempting to do anything else. This can be very restricting because you can't go up to the middle or top of the ladder before ensuring your needs are met at the bottom. Sometimes it's very difficult to talk about your health needs.
> *Michael*

For some young people with health and support needs, their health care needs are the issue that defines their relationship with services. For others, their health care needs are almost made invisible by a focus on their needs for support in their daily lives. For all of them, access to adequate and appropriate health care is crucial to the quality of their lives, and for some of them for their life expectancy.

Most people with physical or sensory impairments and/or learning difficulties have the same kind of health needs as the rest of the population, but they may also have some specific health needs related to their particular impairment or condition. For example, among people with Down's Syndrome there is an above-average incidence of leukaemia, thyroid problems, skin disorder, musculo-skeletal conditions and Alzheimer's disease (Kerr, 1998, p7). People with muscular dystrophy are at greater risk of chest infections than the general population and chest infections pose a greater health risk to them. Some conditions are degenerative and life-limiting. Some conditions are life-threatening if good quality treatment is not available. Some conditions manifest themselves in specific health needs, such as cystic fibrosis, sickle cell disorder, thalassaemia and diabetes.

It is very important, therefore, that as young people make the transition to adulthood they receive information about, and access to, the health care which will make all the difference to the quality of their lives and, in some instances, to their chances of survival. The evidence, however, is that this does not always happen.

An overview of the needs of young people with physical impairments, commissioned by the Department of Health in the early 1990s, concluded:

> 'Currently, the services received by the vast majority
> of these young people are unfocused and fragmented.
> Multidisciplinary, effective inter-agency working is rare.
> The evidence is that these young people have many
> preventable medical problems and a poor quality of life,
> and often fail to reach their potential.'
> (Chamberlain, 1993, para 6)

Similar conclusions have been drawn about the experiences of many young people with significant learning difficulties, particularly those who also have 'challenging behaviour'. The consequences for individuals are illustrated by Doreen's description of her son's health problems as he is growing up. Paul is now 19 and has spent most of his childhood and adolescence at boarding school and a children's home.

'They had been neglecting his health needs. I've had to be cross and say as far as I'm concerned it doesn't matter if Paul is disabled, he still has health care needs. He's 5 feet 11 but his weight fell to 6 stone. He just was not thriving. He regurgitates a lot and nobody was doing anything about it. They kept saying it's something he's learned to do. He's now on this dietary supplement and he is putting weight on and getting a lot stronger.

'His teeth were never taken care of, I don't think he'd ever been taken to the dentist. Now that's being taken care of. He gets a lot of nose bleeds and apparently they had been getting very, very bad and I didn't know about this. When he went to the children's home they took him to the doctor about this and he was put on medication to help, which discoloured his teeth and made him extremely constipated. The trouble is that some of the carers don't look further than their nose. They don't think, if this was my own child would I allow this to go on? I got them to stop the medication because it was really making things worse.

'The other problem he's had is with his legs. When he was at the residential school, for almost seven years, he had no physiotherapy. Because of the way he walks, his backside muscles have wasted away and his hip bone on the right side just sticks out like an elbow. It was neglect that made him like that. I've seen the orthopaedic specialist who says there's nothing he can do because everything had been left too late.'

Young people who need continuing nursing care should
be covered by health authorities' criteria for the provision
of continuing care. However, the Department of Health's
monitoring of their Continuing Care Guidance found that
most authorities had focused on older people and on people
leaving hospital (Department of Health, 1997, Annex A).

Current research on the experiences of health services across
a wide range of different groups of young people seems to
indicate two general problems:

- very patchy provision of health services specifically
  geared to those in **transition to adulthood**

- a lack of specialist provision for some groups of **adults**
  with health care needs and/or inadequate and variable
  access to the specialist provision which exists.

Transition from children's to adults' health services

The way in which a young person is transferred from
children's to adults' services will, to a large extent, determine
the nature of their access to health services throughout most
of their adulthood. Unfortunately, there is evidence that many
young people lose contact with specialist services and/or
move into using general services which do not have sufficient
knowledge and understanding of their particular needs. Ann
Chamberlain's review found that very few health districts
have developed specific transitional services. This, she
believed, has significant consequences:

'Failure to set up transitional services has long-term implications in terms of unfulfilled potential of individuals, a heavy burden of disability and many years of expensive dependency for these young people and their ageing families.' (Chamberlain, 1993, para 14)

Although there have been more transition clinics set up since Chamberlain reported in 1993, the picture is still patchy across the country and many young people have the kind of experience described by Simon:

'When you get to 16 they get rid of you … I haven't been to the hospital for a check-up since I was 16. I know I'm OK at the minute but a lot could happen. No-one's mentioned to me what happens to my condition as I get older, I've got a fair idea but no-one comes up and tells you. I haven't tried to find out more; whatever happens happens.'

Georgina, who also has a neuromuscular condition, was lucky in that, just as she reached adulthood, the hospital where she attended a children's clinic set up a young adults' clinic:

'I've just stopped going to the children's clinic in London. I don't think they really know what to do with you when you get to late teens, early 20s. Now they've just set up a young persons' clinic so I've been transferred into that. It's so much better than going to the children's clinic. I just found it better to go into a normal hospital bit rather than the bit with Beatrix Potter animals painted all over the walls and all the little kids tearing around and screaming. It's quite nice to go to the adults' civilised bit. Also I met a couple of people with the same condition who are about 30 which was a bit more useful because I could talk to them about funding and working.'

Chamberlain's report argued that for

'young disabled persons negotiating the transition from childhood to adulthood, it is recommended that a dedicated community-based team with specific responsibility for this transition be set up. The team should include health and social services professionals.'

Research on young people with cystic fibrosis asked the young people their opinions on 'joint transition clinics', described as clinics where paediatrician and adult physician, and some members of both paediatric and adult teams, were present as part of the preparation for transfer from children's to adults' services.

'The most notable finding in respect of joint transition clinics was that, whether or not people had attended such a clinic, almost 90% thought they were a good idea. Reasons given included familiarity and ease – the supportive aspect of having a person one knows well present when meeting someone new; confidence that information about one's condition and treatment has been conveyed accurately and in a personal way rather than by the mere transfer of notes; and having rumours or fears of the unknown dispelled.' (Pownceby, undated (b), pp20–21)

Pownceby asked young people with cystic fibrosis what kinds of thing helped in the transition from paediatric to adult health services. Factors mentioned included:

- support from paediatric staff and welcome from adult staff

- being able to see the paediatrician by oneself for some time before transfer

- transferring as part of a group of young people

- receiving practical written information about the new centre

- joint clinics

- the opportunity to visit the new centre

- a longer period of preparation for transfer

- the opportunity to talk about doubts and anxieties.

(Pownceby, undated(b) p23)

One concern that young people have following transfer to adult health services is that, when they spend time in hospital, they are likely to be on wards with older people. This was one of the disadvantages reported in a survey of young people with cystic fibrosis (Pownceby, undated (b) p22). A stay in hospital can be quite a shocking experience for some young people, in contrast with the experiences of children's wards. A number of young people in Pownceby's study felt that it would help if there were a young person's ward or unit in the hospital, or at least an 'adolescent room' on the adult ward (Pownceby, undated (b) p23). Health services therefore need to think about in-patient as well as out-patient services to young people.

Are young people's particular needs catered for by health services that are multidisciplinary and focused on transition to adulthood?

Adult services and young people with health and support needs

When Chamberlain looked at services to disabled adults, she found that 'in most districts there is little or no special provision [of health services for disabled people]. This results in increased morbidity and dependence' (Chamberlain, 1993, p6).

Chamberlain's report drew attention to the benefits of specialist and multidisciplinary health care for people with conditions such as epilepsy, referring to evidence that

> 'treatment delivered by a multidisciplinary team is effective in reducing frequency of seizures and rationalised therapy results. Reduced frequency increases the chances of employment; if attacks are eliminated or nocturnal only, driving may be a possibility.' (Chamberlain, 1993, p30)

Yet a review of epilepsy services in 1996 found that recommendations for specialist services made over the last 40 years had still not been fully implemented (Thapar, 1996).

Generally, Chamberlain found that:

'Existing services are used by young people with disabilities in an unfocused and unco-ordinated way. Many lose contact with helping agencies; their health deteriorates, their dependency is increased.' (Chamberlain, 1993, p5)

Evidence concerning the experiences of people with learning difficulties echoes this finding. Michael Kerr concluded from his review of research into primary health care and people with learning difficulties that there is:

- insufficient attention to the health needs of people with learning disability, with a lack of basic health promotion and identification of ill-health

- a range of barriers to the delivery of health care.

(Kerr, 1998, p7)

A project worker on the Changing Days project (run by the King's Fund), which is concerned with enabling people with learning difficulties to participate in their local communities, said that often 'people aren't well enough to live ordinary lives'.

Generally the barriers to good quality health care – experienced in common by people with widely different impairments and conditions – include the following:

- Access to primary health care may be poor because the service creates barriers. For example, a GP may not take the time to understand someone with a communication impairment; some young people with high medical needs are not able to register with their local GP – one local authority reported that a group home set up for people with continuing health care needs found that the local GP refused to allow them to register with him.

- One label gets in the way of recognising other needs; for example, a failure to recognise sight problems in people with learning difficulties or, if they are recognised, failure to address them seriously, from eye tests to cataract operations. The RNIB says 'Unfortunately, people with learning difficulties frequently go through their lives unnecessarily handicapped because staff and carers have not tried to obtain appropriate eye care – or do not know how to get help' (RNIB Multiple Disability Services, 1998, p3).

- Once young people leave paediatric services, many of them lose contact with specialist health care. Michelle lost contact with specialist health services when she reached 19, and it is likely that her incontinence problems are related to lack of specialist advice about catheter management. She explained how 'over the years my bladder shrunk to almost nothing because of having an indwelling catheter'.

- A lack of understanding by health care professionals of specific conditions. For example, young people with diabetes spoke of how general practitioners often had little knowledge about their condition, and they would prefer to attend specialist clinics – 'I'd rather see someone who knows what they're talking about' (Olsen & Sutton, 1996, pp16–17). Michael Kerr found that many general practitioners fail to recognise the need for screening for hypothyroidism in people with Down's Syndrome. Charlotte, who has ME, talked about how 'devastating' she finds it that doctors do not understand her condition: 'My GP tries very hard to be supportive but it is obvious that he knows little about severe ME which means that I can't really trust him and he can't fully support me'. Judith Cavet's research on children and young people with chronic faecal incontinence found that local health services were not geared up to meet their needs (Cavet, 1998).

There seem to be particular issues to do with medication and people with learning difficulties. Service responses to 'challenging behaviour' among adults are more likely to involve medication than among children. Transition to adulthood may therefore be a crucial period for determining the kinds of response that will dominate people's adult lives. In one study of people with learning difficulties and challenging behaviour:

> 'Despite relatively low levels of mental illness, just over half (52%) of adults showing challenging behaviour were taking antipsychotic drugs. This compares with one in four (27%) who were said by staff to be subject to "an agreed written behaviour modification programme".'
> (Qureshi, 1994, p31)

Children were less likely to be given drugs to control their behaviour (18%) than to be subject to a behaviour modification programme (60%).

Listening to young people

Barbara, whose behaviour has posed difficulties for others, feels that as she grew older she was consulted more about the medication she was prescribed:

> 'Until I was 19, I was never consulted about my medication and I wasn't interested in asking, I just took it. Now when I get medication through my GP he talks to me about it. I feel I have choices. He prescribed me this medication because I needed help with feeling stressed. He said, it will make you feel more relaxed. When I saw him last week he said how are you getting on and I said all right but I feel a bit sleepy. He said all right, have half a tablet in the morning and half a tablet in the afternoon. It still makes me sleepy, though. I've got to go back in three months' time.'

However, a number of the young people who were interviewed for this report described difficult experiences in their interaction with medical professionals. As Brian said:

> 'When I used to go up to London to the specialist, there used to be a room full of students and the professor would be saying "feel this" because I used to get a lot of spasm and stuff. He wanted the students to feel what it felt like. It was quite horrible really.'

Michelle's similar experiences were made worse because it was a male doctor:

'For years it's been male doctors. They're doctors and
they prod me, I hate it. They throw the classic line, the
doctors don't see you as a woman but that might be how
they feel but I don't. It might not make any difference to
them but it does to me.'

Children and young people with haemoglobinopathy
reported the importance of front-line health staff talking to
them, being knowledgeable about the condition, and
respecting the young person's own knowledge about their
condition and needs (Atkin & Ahmad, 1998, pp29–30). Young
people with diabetes reported that specialists in hospital
clinics sometimes did not seem to acknowledge young
people's own expertise. One young man said, 'In hospitals
they seem to be "I know it all, you don't, this is my hospital"'
(Olsen & Sutton, 1996, pp16–17).

A number of the young people interviewed for this report had
strong opinions about the importance of health professionals
listening to them. As Ruth said:

'I think doctors and nurses should listen to us as people,
not just as someone using the services. At the end of the
day, we're using the service because we've got a chronic
condition that's life-threatening and they should listen to
us and not just administer drugs to us. For example, if
they're building a new unit, they should listen to our
opinions, like we'd like a kitchen on the ward because an
awful lot of time we don't eat very well and it'd be nice to
have a kitchen with a microwave where us as patients

can go in and make our own little meal. And basic things like having locks on toilet doors in the children's hospital.'

And Georgina said:

'If anyone were to ask me what message I might have for others, I would tell them that they should listen to, believe and respect young people. In my experience it is very difficult to tell anyone how you feel when they won't listen; if you aren't believed then you stop believing in yourself; if you're not respected then you lose your self-respect and everyone needs self-respect.'

Physiotherapy

While many young disabled people who attended special schools complain about the amount of time taken away from their education by physiotherapy, most of them find that physiotherapy stops once they leave school and some of them feel that their health and/or physical ability suffers as a result. Ninety-six percent of people responding to a survey carried out by the newspaper *Disability Now* felt they needed physiotherapy and were either not getting it or not getting enough of it (*Disability Now*, February 1999, p10).

Lois was alert to her daughter's continuing need for physiotherapy once she left residential school and ensured that this was included in her health care assessment. She said:

'We had a review last week when Phillipa had been at the bungalow for a month and I talked about the need for ongoing physiotherapy support. I got the impression from the community nurse that a lot of work would be done now by the professionals but then they would hope that the care staff would just continue with the physiotherapy. She's got another review when she's been there three months and we will talk about it again then. I think they see their input as temporary, but we shall be making the point that Phillipa has been assessed as Category 3 in terms of her health needs assessment – which means "intensive support, regular visits by health team professionals" and it defines "regular" as being not less than once every seven days and it says it's not time-limited.'

Phillipa is lucky that her mother is well-informed and persistent in her struggle to get the best service for her daughter. One of the major difficulties with accessing physiotherapy as an adult is that the services seem to assume that physiotherapy is time-limited and geared towards 'rehabilitation'. This was Georgina's experience as she grew up. Now a 22-year-old student at art college, she said:

'Physio is a bit of a problem. When I was a kid I used to get physio all the time but as soon as I stopped being in the child bracket then they didn't really have space for me as an adult. I used to go to the children's clinic at the local hospital, physio once a week and hydrotherapy once a week, out of school hours and arranged by my GP. But that all stopped when I got to about 16. Recently, I got my GP to refer me for the Easter holidays just so that I could go and do some hydrotherapy but in the adult bit. But the people there were accident victims and that kind of thing, with quite different needs to mine. My needs are more to keep moving rather than to see any improvement. I could only get to do hydrotherapy for a limited period, like for four weeks, and they weren't familiar at all with my needs because they don't normally deal with someone like me. When I finish college and go back to live in that area I feel I'd like to have more hydrotherapy but I'm not sure that they will let me go indefinitely.'

> **How can health commissioners ensure that young people with continuing health care needs do not cease to receive the treatment they need (such as access to specialist consultant or to services such as physiotherapy) merely because they have moved out of paediatric services?**

Communication needs

> Many times I could not put forward my ideas, opinions
> or feelings because there was not enough help with
> my board.
> *Susan*

Some people have communication needs which are
'complex' because they use methods which are unfamiliar to
others. This can mean their communication needs are unmet
and their frustration can result in behaviour which is difficult
for others to deal with. Many people whose behaviour is
difficult for others to cope with have a range of impairments.
Sensory and communication impairments can make people
very vulnerable to situations where they don't know what is
going on, where things are done against their wishes or
where their needs are not responded to.

As the RNIB's Multiple Disability Service points out:

> 'In the past, there was a tendency to assume that people
> behaved in particular ways because of who they were,
> rather than looking at where they were and how they might
> be responding to their environment, the people around
> them and inappropriate support or lack of stimulation …
> RNIB believes that much challenging behaviour is
> "environmentally produced". That is, challenging
> behaviour should be seen as a form of terrorism – fighting
> against an unresponsive system, people coping in their
> own way in settings which do not cater for their individual
> needs.' (RNIB Focus Factsheet, undated, p5)

In recent years there has been important questioning of the way people with 'challenging behaviour' are perceived. This questioning springs from thinking about people in terms of their human rights. As Mary Myers says:

'The basic question is: do we believe that the individual who performs bizarre and frightening acts is nevertheless a full human being, one of us, with reasons for the behaviours, and in need of help to live among us? Or do we, in our hearts – however kind – really believe that "they" must be fundamentally different from "us", as past adjectives, "defective" and "subnormal" emphasised? It is the answer to this question that will dictate the foundations and directions of service developments.' (Myers, 1995, pp262–263)

There have been a number of developments in recent years which focus on people as individuals and on their experiences. One important example comes from Phoebe Caldwell, who promotes an approach that is about relationships:

'It aims to shift our attention away from the problems a person presents to the difficulties they experience. Bearing in mind that current service provision is unable to reach these people, this approach is predicated on a radical change in values. In order to get in touch, we must cease trying to bend their behaviours to our world and enter their world, as they experience it.' (Caldwell, 1998, p4)

Yet it is clear that more dissemination of good practice is required. The RNIB's experience is that:

> 'Many staff who contact RNIB's Information and Practice Development Service on Multiple Disability seem to believe that "good" service-users are passive and do not make demands, and simply wait for things to happen.' (RNIB Focus Factsheet, undated, p12)

In 1994, the Social Services Inspectorate held a workshop on developing community services for people with 'complex multiple disabilities' (Social Services Inspectorate, 1995b). This followed their report of an inspection of services, *Whose Life is it, Anyway?* which 'confirmed the low priority status of adults with multiple impairments, lack of professional awareness and the acute need for responsive services' (Social Services Inspectorate, 1992).

The SSI also published some good practice examples of how methods such as 'person-centred planning' can increase communication and understanding about individuals' needs, even when they have significant learning difficulties and communication impairments. One example concerned a man called Keith Allez: 'Although Keith's keyworker believed he knew Keith well, person-centred planning uncovered new insights about Keith and re-discovered some knowledge that had been lost' (Social Services Inspectorate, 1996b, p11).

This included vital information about how Keith communicated when he needed to go to the toilet; the 'new knowledge' meant that Keith became continent. At the point when the person-centred planning was done for Keith, he was in transition, moving from a hostel into his own home. The method is equally appropriate for young people during transition to adulthood, as this is a period when they are likely to experience a number of moves and changes in the people around them.

Indeed, transition to adulthood can mean losing touch with the people who know how the young person communicates. The Changing Days project, run by the King's Fund, has found that, for example, methods of communication used by the young person's teachers are lost when s/he transfers to a day centre. The project has highlighted some good practice examples of using 'circles of support' to bring together everyone who knows the young person well in order to build up a picture of their needs and plan their future. Another initiative is the multimedia profiling developed by the London-based organisation Acting Up. This is an audiovisual diary, using video, photographs, sound, graphics and text, of daily activities and personal history, and has been successful in involving people with 'severe learning disabilities' in person-centred planning.

> **Do service providers know enough about what works in facilitating communication, particularly for people with 'challenging behaviour'? Is there enough dissemination of what works?**

Some young people with significant communication impairments live in residential settings where staff turnover is high and training on communication rare. Phoebe Caldwell's work illustrates the importance and effectiveness of training, for both managers and the (usually unqualified) staff who work directly with people. She also emphasises how training can be put into daily practice and how changes in practice can be maintained (Caldwell, 1998, pp77–81). This emphasis on communication is cost-effective and transforms the lives of the people concerned; it should therefore be an important part of any commissioning strategy, service contract or service development.

> **Do commissioning strategies and service developments for people with 'challenging behaviour' and/or 'multiple impairments' include resources allocated to ongoing training of managers and careworkers?**

Young people may need communication aids, and it is not clear who is responsible for funding, maintaining and up-dating them. Evidence from the young people interviewed for this review, and from some of the service providers interviewed, is that many young people are paying for communication equipment themselves (or their families are) or they have to raise money through charities. There is confusion over whether social, health, education or employment services have statutory duties in this area. Young people may continue using the equipment they were issued with at school, and not have access to up-dated technology and methods. A joint commissioning group for one of the local authorities consulted had identified a specific budget for communication equipment for young adults, but it was not clear whether any of the other five social services and health authorities recognised this essential need.

> **Do commissioning strategies identify resources for the assessment of communication needs and provision of equipment and aids for young people?**

Leisure, friends and relationships

I want to go out more.
Jennifer

Research into the experiences of young disabled people has consistently found that they have fewer opportunities for friendships and leisure activities than their non-disabled peers, and that the more significant the impairment, the more limited their relationships and activities (Hirst & Baldwin, 1994; Flynn & Hirst, 1992).

Young people who leave residential school often lose contact with the friends that they have grown up with, particularly if they have communication impairments that make it difficult to use the telephone. Robert, now aged 22 and living in a shared bungalow attached to a residential home, talked about how he had lost contact with his best friend when he left residential school at the age of 19:

'We knew each other when we were little, when we first went to school, when we were eight. I left the same time as he did and that was it. He went one way and I went the other way and then that was it. There was nothing in the middle. As he went that way I went the other way, and that was it.'

Jennifer had a similar experience:

'I only keep in touch with one friend from school...When we all left school it was hard to keep in touch. We all went to different places and I can't speak to people on the telephone.'

Young people living in residential settings often also find that members of staff become important to them, but then they lose contact when they or the member of staff move on. Matthew said:

'I want to write to Karl who used to do activities here. I want to tell him what I've been doing...Karl used to do woodwork here. He's not here any more. I miss him. He was my friend.'

Doing things you enjoy with people you like is an important part of most young people's lives, but young disabled people are commonly denied these opportunities and their 'personal and social development' suffers as a result. As the Changing Days project says:

'It is disappointing that services, on the whole, continue to act as if friendship was a relatively unimportant fringe activity. They seem to be so caught up in the 'bricks and mortar' side of providing services that relationships are largely overlooked – and hardly ever invested in. Staff are not given the time or the opportunity to help people develop a wider network of friends outside services.' (*Changing Days Bulletin*, August 1997, p15)

One of the most disabling things for young people who need assistance is to have to rely on the goodwill of others in order to do ordinary things like arrange a day out with friends.

Robert, aged 22 and living in a shared bungalow attached to a residential home, wants to go to the races but cannot unless he persuades a volunteer worker at the home to provide the assistance needed:

> 'I'm trying to organise something with one of the drivers, to see if he doesn't mind. I'm trying to see whether he could take us to the racecourse. It's not far, about five minutes away.'

In most residential services leisure activities of this kind are – if they happen at all – an optional extra, yet such things are crucial to the quality of people's lives.

There is very little research highlighting the barriers to making and maintaining friendships experienced by young people with high levels of health and support needs. Most projects that support friendships and social activities for people with learning difficulties are, as the Changing Days project has found, time-limited and under-funded.

There is even less known about the experiences that young people with health and support needs have around sexuality and sexual relationships. We might assume that they have a need for information and reassurance. For example, an organisation representing young people who use artificial nutrition, consulted during the course of doing this review, reported that concerns over sexual relationships were a major issue that came up in discussions with young people. Some young people are worried about whether anyone will find them sexually attractive. As one young man put it:

'They give us sex education lessons at school but don't give us the chance to talk about whether anyone's ever going to fancy someone in a wheelchair.' (Morris, 1999)

Jennifer is no different from many other young women her age; she wants a sexual relationship but there are many barriers that get in the way:

'My boyfriend lives with his dad. I knew him at school. I've only seen him once since we left. I want to see him more. We can't write to each other or use the telephone.'

One project consulted young disabled people about what would help them to have more confidence about sexual relationships. They came up with 'the 5 Rs':

- Role models in the media and from disabled adults

- a Range of living options and choices

- a Rights model of assistance which comes 'without strings'

- Responsibility for running things

- Real conversations about both sexuality and disability.

(Brown *et al.*, forthcoming)

Recognition of the importance of friendships and sexual relationships for young people with health and support needs will have implications for the kinds of accommodation and support services commissioned. Young people may wish to share a house with their friends, rather than be 'slotted into' a 'bedspace' with other 'service users'; they may wish to live with a partner, and they may become parents.

Some young people, particularly those with significant learning difficulties, are 'slotted into' adult day services when they leave children's services. The Social Services Inspectorate's report on day services for people with learning difficulties found little evidence of strategic planning by social services authorities, and the potential for joint planning and joint work (including joint assessments) between day services and local colleges was underdeveloped (Social Services Inspectorate, 1995c). This inspection also found

> 'little evidence that recreation and leisure were being used effectively to promote the personal and social development of individuals thereby enhancing their capacity to achieve optimal levels of independence.'
> (Social Services Inspectorate, 1995c, p1)

Many of the young people interviewed for this report talked about the difficulties they had in getting transport, and the barrier this was to participation in leisure activities. Brian currently lives in a residential home which, like so many, is in a rural area. He said:

> 'I want to move into the city rather than being in a rural area. I want somewhere you don't have to depend on transport quite so much. Here you have to depend on the van [belonging to the Home] all the time, and help being available ... It'll be so much easier to get to places in the city, I can get a taxi easier. It would cost a bomb to get a taxi from here.'

116

Yasmin, also living in a residential home, communicated how problems with transport get in the way of her doing the things she enjoys:

> 'I like going shopping, to clothes shops. I like music, rock music. But the problem was the taxi business. It is very difficult to get transport…I like going to the cinema. I would like to go out more.'

Transport is discussed in more detail later in this report.

For young people who live in residential settings and who need someone to accompany them when they go out, a perpetual problem is the shortage of staff. Matthew talked about the impact of this on him:

> 'I like going out to my Nan's. I go out and see my brother, Mark. I like bowling. I go out with Simon, he takes a group of us in the bus. We go swimming as well. I would like to go out more. The weather can stop me going out, or short [shortage of] staff. When someone phones in sick there's no activities. Then I'm disappointed.'

Michelle had hoped that moving into a bedsit attached to a residential home would give her greater freedom and ability to socialise than she had previously had:

> 'I was very isolated. Transport was a major problem – if you could get the vehicle you couldn't get the driver – "we're short-staffed"… Although I saw it [moving into

the bedsit] as a new start, it hasn't been that – it's the same short-staffing, no transport and I still feel isolated.'

She concluded:

'To begin with I was very tolerant of them saying "I'm sorry, I can't do that at the moment, we're short-staffed". That saying has followed me around ever since, I should have it engraved on my heart.'

Do your commissioning strategies and accommodation and support services recognise the importance of leisure activities, friendships and sexual relationships in young people's lives?

Do your commissioning strategies and service developments include the aims of tackling the barriers to friendships and leisure activities encountered by young people with health and support needs?

Have you addressed the needs for information and support that young people might have around sexuality and sexual relationships?

Employment and other opportunities

> I did a work placement and I got so much hassle
> from the people working there.
> *Simon*

> Why should I pay out of my wages to be got up
> in the morning?
> *Georgina*

For most young people, entry into paid work is a key part of their transition to adulthood. However, for some young people who have health and support needs, employment may not be an option. This is not always because of their levels of impairment or the nature of their condition, but rather because of prejudicial attitudes and lack of access to the support they need. Michael, for example, described how his personal assistance needs were not met when he went on work experience:

> 'While I was at college I did work experience with the police. The problem with that, though, was my care needs. I had to take my own care staff to help me with going to the toilet and the college said they couldn't spare the staff just to work with me. So I had to give up the work experience.'

In a sample of 104 young people with cystic fibrosis, two thirds of those who had left full-time education were unemployed (Pownceby, undated (b) p4); this is the same level of unemployment experienced by disabled people generally. Discriminatory attitudes are likely to play a large part in creating this situation, as Ruth – who has cystic fibrosis and eventually got a job after a great deal of difficulty – found:

> 'Previous to this job I applied for a lot of jobs. I used to write down "asthma" on application forms and even just saying asthma I didn't get an interview. I'd be writing down the same GCSEs as my friends and they'd get a job and I didn't even get an interview. And if I got an interview and then mentioned I got cystic fibrosis, I never got a job. So I think there's a lot of prejudice around.'

It is now unlawful for an employer to discriminate against a disabled person (*Disability Discrimination Act 1995*, Sections 4 and 5). However, as with leisure activities, friendships and sexual relationships, we know very little about the experiences of people with high levels of health and/or support needs in terms of their opportunities for employment and whether the *Disability Discrimination Act* is making any difference to these opportunities.

Some young people fear that a history of illness will mean that employers continue to discriminate against them even when they are recovered. As Charlotte, who has ME, said, 'My concern is that employers won't want me when they realise that I've had an illness which (unless a cure is found) could always reappear'. This may also be a concern for young people who have had cancer. It is not clear yet whether the *Disability Discrimination Act* will be effective in preventing such discrimination.

Unequal access to employment can also result from the way the social security system operates, and the way accommodation and support are funded. A review of research on supported living and supported employment for people with learning difficulties highlighted a number of barriers, including disincentives to making the transition from Incapacity Benefit to paid employment and the very patchy funding of supported employment initiatives (Simons, 1998).

People who have high personal assistance needs face a major disincentive to paid employment because the funding of personal assistance through the Independent Living Fund is means-tested. As Ann Kestenbaum points out, anyone in receipt of an ILF grant retains only £30 per week more than Income Support levels if they take paid employment (Kestenbaum, 1998). Local authority social services departments are also increasingly charging for services and using a means test to determine how much and whether someone should pay. A number are also applying charging policies to direct payments. All this, together with the disincentives created by the Housing Benefit system, means that paid employment is rarely a financially viable option for people with high support needs. This is something that Georgina, an art student who employs personal assistants, is very aware of as she contemplates her options when she leaves college:

'The problem is funding for my personal assistants. If I got a traditional kind of job I'd lose some of my funding. That's concerning me a bit. I think it's really unfair – why should I pay out of my wages to be got up in the morning? So I'm not really thinking of a traditional kind of job.'

> ## Do your charging policies for community care services act as a barrier to paid employment?

A recent review of research on employment and disabled people established that most employment projects focus on training and entering work, rather than on sustaining employment (Barnes *et al.*, 1998). This is a major issue for people with continuing health needs, but there has been little attention paid to the barriers they face in retaining a job and what forms of support are useful.

> ## Do your health and social services commissioning strategies include working with employment services?

Where paid employment is difficult to achieve, day services have an important role to play in making it possible for young people to do other meaningful activities which promote community integration and personal development. The Changing Days project, a joint initiative by the King's Fund and the National Development Team, seeks to shift day services for adults with learning difficulties from 'services based on containment and segregation to services centred on individual needs and community inclusion'.

This means moving resources from buildings-based provision to enable people to do the things they enjoy doing. For example, Sunderland Social Services closed one of its five day centres and used the revenue:

- to increase the number of staff hours in small residential homes to improve the quality of people's day and evening activities

- to set up a theatre arts workshop and a horticultural service

- to pay for 100 hours a week of individualised support to people to participate in mainstream activities

- to set up a supported employment service.

(*Changing Days Bulletin*, August 1997, p5)

Recognising that there are increasing numbers of people with high support needs using services, including those who use non-verbal methods of communication, the Changing Days project emphasises that a key principle is to 'meet the special needs of each person in the least special way' (*Changing Days Bulletin*, August 1997, p10). This is an extremely important starting point in respect of the needs of young people who have complex needs; applying the philosophy of inclusion to them does not mean failing to recognise that they have particular needs. Rather, it means meeting their needs in a way which is most likely to include them in their local communities and enable them to do the kinds of thing their non-disabled peers do.

> **When commissioning and developing adult day services, do you aim to enable people to participate in their local communities? Are resources and support focused on tackling the barriers individuals face to doing the things they enjoy doing?**

In recent years, family support services for children and education services have addressed the need to develop policies and practices which would make it possible for children with continuing health care needs to use these services. The Department for Education and Department of Health have issued joint guidance on 'supporting pupils with medical needs' and Barnardo's has developed guidelines for family support services to children who need 'invasive clinical procedures' (Department for Education/Department of Health, 1996; Rhodes *et al.*, 1998). It is not clear whether such progress has also been made in further and higher education and in adult day services.

Lois found that it was possible to find a residential placement for her daughter which also included day-time activities specifically tailored to meet Phillipa's needs:

> 'The day-time activities are organised individually for each person according to their assessments – Phillipa does aromatherapy, and she goes to a couple of sensory units.'

On the other hand, Jennifer has been 'slotted in' to a day centre twice a week and has little choice over how she spends her time:

> 'I did cooking at school. I wanted to carry on doing that. I don't get the chance to do cooking now. I told them at the day centre but I can't do it there.'

Susan, who, like Jennifer, lives in a residential home and does not use speech to communicate, is clear that she wants to do more things with her life:

> 'I want to do more work with the Touch Talker and the computer. I want to do photography, art, interaction skills.'

Mobility and transport

> I like going to the cinema. I would like to go out more.
> *Yasmin*

Many young people's opportunities are limited by the availability of equipment to aid their mobility and of transport to get to the places they want to go to. Research for Scope confirms the difficulties that disabled people generally have with getting the equipment they need (Marks, 1998). A number of young people interviewed for this report had purchased their wheelchairs privately or through charities. Brian had to 'fundraise from charities' to buy an indoor/outdoor electric wheelchair and Simon's experience is not unusual:

> 'I bought my electric wheelchair myself. The wheelchair voucher scheme in this area is a waste of time because the wheelchairs under the scheme are just useless. They say you have to go to the hospital and we'll tell you what you need. But I know what I need. This wheelchair cost me £4,500.'

The RNIB has drawn attention to the way that 'ordinary mobility aids' (for people with physical impairments) are often not provided for blind and partially-sighted people, particularly if they also have learning difficulties. When wheelchairs are provided, they are very rarely self-propelling or electric. The RNIB commented:

126

'When we questioned the wisdom of this, we were told very firmly that blind people expect to be pushed – and therefore do not need self-propelling chairs…Yet there are visually disabled people with learning difficulties "bombing" around in electric wheelchairs. Sometimes staff find this hard to believe…' (RNIB, 1998, p5)

Lack of transport can have a significant impact on young people's opportunities for leisure activities and making and maintaining friendships. As Louise, who lives in a residential home, said, 'I have to plan in advance my transport and a carer…My transport is paid for by myself which can get quite expensive'.

Some people are able to drive themselves but find it very difficult to get their own vehicle, suitably adapted, particularly if they have to rely on a grant from Motability to fund the adaptations. Simon described his experience:

'It's taken me four years so far…I've had to go through assessments, I've had three vehicles offered to me which have been no good whatsoever. They said I should have a vehicle that had no lift for me to get into in the wheelchair. I would have had to have someone to help me get in and to get the wheelchair in and out. It was ridiculous, I would have had a vehicle sitting out there which I couldn't use. But they've just agreed now that I should have the one with a lift and I've got to go down to the assessment place one more time and it should then all go through.'

127

Yasmin, however, can only dream about having more freedom to go out:

> 'It would be nice if my mum and dad got me a van. They've been talking about it ever since I was at the other home but nothing's happened yet.'

Lack of transport and mobility equipment can impede access to further and higher education and employment. The Snowden Award Scheme (which gives grants to students who need help with costs associated with impairment in order to pursue further education or training) has found that there are rising numbers of people looking for help with travel costs and mobility aids (Stone *et al.*, 1998, p59).

Do your commissioning strategies include access to transport and the provision of equipment to aid mobility?

Consultation and involvement

> I want them to know how much it pissed me off that they
> would always talk to my mother rather than to me. I want
> them to know I have a voice – don't speak to others,
> speak to me.
> *Brian*

Most of the young people interviewed for this report had
clear views on how organisations and professionals could do
things better. All of the local authorities said consultation with
young people was an area that could be improved upon. 'This
is an area we need to develop', said one. What consultation
there was tended to be with parents and to concern particular
service provision, such as family-based care, day services, or
general consultation on community care plans. One local
authority reported that people with learning difficulties were
represented on a joint planning group but they did not often
attend 'due to lack of support to attend and/or debriefing'.
Another said that:

> 'We do want to consider something under Best Value,
> but at present consultation is individual and anecdotal
> and carers/family views can dominate.'

Nevertheless, there are a few examples of genuine
consultation with people who have high levels of need.
Newham People First, for example, has been involved in
discussions about the commissioning of services, in a review
of day services and in the inspection of group homes. Funded
by health and social services, the project ensures that the

129

voice of people with learning difficulties – including those with 'multiple impairments' – is heard by changing consultation methods to suit the service users (Newham People First, 1998).

Direct accounts, such as those obtained from the 14 young people interviewed for this report, can contain powerful and important messages for those who commission and provide services. Health care professionals, for example, need to hear what it feels like to be on the receiving end of treatment, as Simon describes:

> 'They used to make me walk up and down, poke you about, see how far you can walk before you collapse. Then they'd sit you in your chair and make you sit in the waiting room until another doctor wanted to look at you.'

One project which works with young people with learning difficulties found that, when they were asked about their dreams and ambitions, their aspirations were remarkably similar to those of their non-disabled peers, yet their experiences were very different. As the authors concluded:

> 'There is a wide disparity between these young people's past and present life experiences and their future ambitions. Their accounts bring home to us, if we did not already know, that most young people with learning difficulties do not wish to lead segregated lives, diverging from their non-disabled peers in life experiences and everyday activities. Yet these young people and others like them are ill-prepared to achieve their aspirations,

because of their experiences of segregated schooling, widespread exclusion from the job market, and by the negative attitudes, and sometimes outright hostility, of others. It is only when these disabling barriers are overcome that they will have the same sort of chances as other young people to realise their ambitions.' (The Leighton Project with Simon Grant & Daisy Cole, 1998, p188)

People who have high levels of support needs and/or continuing health care needs will have particular requirements if they are to be involved in any consultation exercise. The Leonard Cheshire Disabled People's Forum, for example, found that people living in residential care need to be provided with personal assistance and transport if they are to come to meetings; the Cystic Fibrosis Trust makes use of teleconferencing in order to overcome the dangers of cross-infection; the Association of Youth with ME has developed methods of involving young people who cannot leave their homes.

The Nuffield Community Care Studies Unit carried out a piece of work for Leicestershire Health, which used focus groups of young people with diabetes. The usefulness of this approach was illustrated by the three main questions raised by the young people's experiences and opinions, which have both general implications for the planning of services for all young people with continuing health care needs and specific implications for those with diabetes (Olsen & Sutton, 1996, pp26–27). These questions were:

- 'Do we need to make expertise more flexible?'. In other words, how can the provision of expert advice and specialist treatment be made more accessible and suited to individual lifestyles?

- 'Do we need to make flexibility more expert?'. In other words, how can the existing most accessible services be utilised to deliver specialist advice and treatment?

- 'Should we re-think the interface between paediatric and adult diabetes services?'. Young adults seem to be in need of particular forms of support because of specific needs related to transition to adulthood – neither children's nor adults' services are appropriate for this age group.

Some organisations representing people with continuing health care needs have developed projects which aim to increase people's involvement in treatment and decisions about services. The CF Advocacy project, for example, aims

> 'to give people with CF a voice in the services they use …
> A major part of the advocate's job is to find out what their
> fellow patients feel about what happens at clinic, on the
> ward and with regard to home support, and to represent
> their views to the appropriate authorities.'
> (*CF News*, Summer 1998)

The advocates act as a channel of communication between individual patients and the CF health professionals:

'Clinical nurse specialists in particular have welcomed the fact that people will tell the advocate about problems which they would previously have harboured, and these can be dealt with before they become crises.'
(*CF News*, Summer 1998)

They also represent the concerns of patients as a group to the health trusts/health authorities.

Self-help groups and local disability organisations are important resources for consultation and involvement initiatives. Commissioners need to draw on both the specialist expertise of national organisations concerned with specific impairments and conditions, and local organisations which – properly resourced – can be valuable channels of communication with users of services.

> **Are the views and experiences of young people with health and support needs sought during planning and commissioning? Are a variety of methods of consultation used?**

Conclusion

If anyone were to ask me what message I might have for others I would tell them that they should listen to, believe and respect young people.
Charlotte

I think the most important thing for professionals to do is not to have any preconceived ideas about what you can do or what you should be allowed to try.
Georgina

Making my own decisions is very important to me.
Simon

I wanted them to know I have a voice – don't speak to others, speak to me.
Brian

This review concerns a group of young people who have a wide range of conditions and impairments but whose common characteristic is that they all require a combination of health and support services in order to access a good quality of life. There is evidence that many of these young people experience a failure of health and social services to meet their needs as they grow into adulthood. They are at risk of being socially excluded by services which segregate them from the rest of society and which pay inadequate attention to needs arising from poor health and/or mobility, sensory, cognitive and communication impairments.

Yet young people with 'complex needs' have ambitions like anyone else. Twenty-four-year-old Louise, who has mobility and visual impairments and has had mental health difficulties, who has been living in residential care since she left school, says:

> 'I still hope to share a place one day with someone, and to go to Australia.'

The background to this review has been the various Government initiatives that recognise that there should be an integrated approach to both the commissioning and the provision of services to people with health and support needs. Legislation has been introduced to create:

- pooled budgets between health and social services authorities

- lead commissioning, where one authority takes responsibility and also holds the funds for purchasing both health and social care

- integrated provision, where one organisation provides both health and social care.

A more integrated approach to both commissioning and the provision of services would certainly make a difference to young people who have health and support needs. However, the fragmentation in responses to their needs is caused not only by the current divisions between health and social services but also by:

- inadequate liaison with housing, leisure, education and employment services

- the experience of being transferred from children's to adults' services in health and social services organisations.

Those responsible for commissioning services for this group of young people often have inadequate and incomplete information about what is required, and what information does exist tends to be based on diagnoses or service categories rather than generated by the actual needs of the young people concerned.

If services are to make a difference to the lives of young people, we need to start from the experiences of young people themselves. Perhaps the clearest message from them is that they want the same things that any young person wants as they grow into adulthood: they want friends, sex, money, a place to call their own, and the freedom to do the things they enjoy doing. Sometimes their state of health or an impairment means that they require additional services and support in order to achieve these things. Sometimes, unfortunately, the way services are delivered actually creates a barrier to achieving these things.

The Government's White Paper, *Modernising Social Services*, set out three priority areas for change in services for adults:

- promoting independence

- improving consistency

- providing convenient, user-centred services.

Together with a more integrated approach to meeting people's needs, these principles would address many of the issues raised in this report. However, there is a danger that young people will continue to fall between children's and adults' services in terms of the new developments around modernising health and social services.

While the development of national priorities for health and social care, performance standards and targets, the Quality Protects initiative and Best Value performance management arrangements all involve aims which are relevant to young people with 'complex health and support needs', these initiatives are currently focused predominantly on older people, children looked after and users of mental health services. Understandable though this is, young people in transition to adulthood are in danger of experiencing a transition to social exclusion if their needs are not better addressed.

This report has attempted to identify some detailed questions which would help those commissioning and providing services to focus resources better on improving the quality of life of young people who need support if they are to achieve what our society wants for all young people. The report therefore concludes with listing these questions.

Questions for those commissioning and providing services

Information required for commissioning services

Do you have common definitions and ways of gathering information about young people with health and support needs, which have been agreed by all local agencies?

Have you recognised that there are increasing numbers of young people:

- with a range of impairments
- with conditions which are life-limiting and who require continuing health care?

Are you gathering information about young people's needs?

Are you measuring service outcomes in terms of what differences services make to young people's lives?

Information to young people and their families

Do you know what information young people want? Do you have a strategy for providing this information? Does the information include:

- what young people are entitled to under relevant legislation and local policies?

- what services are provided by all parts of the statutory sector – health, education, housing, leisure, social services, employment services?

- what services are provided by the voluntary and private sector?

- details of national and local self-help and representative groups?

Emotional support

Do your commissioning strategies and plans for service development include the provision of emotional support to young people and their families?

Do you recognise that parents are often an important source of emotional support and assist parents to provide this support?

Do you recognise the support that young people get from each other and nurture this form of support?

Are counselling and psychological support services available for young people to address issues relating to living with life-limiting and life-threatening conditions? Are resources put into setting up support groups?

Are counselling and psychological support services available for young people, including those with communication impairments and/or 'challenging behaviour'?

Advocacy, mentoring and peer support

Do you have a strategy for providing advocacy services for young people, including those with significant communication impairments?

Do you draw on the expertise of individuals with health and support needs, and voluntary organisations representing them, to provide advocacy, mentoring and peer support?

Education

Do your joint commissioning strategies and mechanisms include the provision of education within their remit, and involve education agencies?

Does transition planning for young people include continuing access to education?

Accommodation and support

What arrangements are there to ensure that the housing requirements of young people with health and support needs are addressed in the drawing up of local housing strategies?

Do allocation policies give full recognition to the needs and circumstances of young people with health and support needs?

Is there a local commissioning strategy to enable young people with health and support needs to live 'ordinary lives' in their local communities?

Do mechanisms for monitoring services, and reviews of individual placements, measure the extent to which young people can live 'ordinary lives' in their local communities?

Do commissioning strategies address the particular accommodation and support needs of people with 'multiple impairments' and those with continuing health care needs who do not fall within any of the traditional service headings?

What arrangements are there for joint commissioning of accommodation and support services for young people with health and support needs?

Health

Are young people's particular needs catered for by health services which are multidisciplinary and focused on transition to adulthood?

What action is taken to ensure that young people with continuing health care needs do not cease to receive the treatment they need (such as access to specialist consultants, or to services such as physiotherapy) merely because they have moved out of paediatric services?

Communication

Do service providers know enough about what works in facilitating communication, particularly for people with 'challenging behaviour'? Is there enough dissemination of what works?

Do commissioning strategies and service developments for people with 'challenging behaviour' and/or 'multiple impairments' include resources allocated to ongoing training of managers and care workers?

Do your commissioning strategies identify resources for the assessment of communication needs and provision of equipment and aids for young people?

Leisure, friends and relationships

Do your commissioning strategies and accommodation and support services recognise the importance of leisure activities, friendships and sexual relationships in young people's lives?

Do your commissioning strategies and service developments include the aims of tackling the barriers to friendships and leisure activities encountered by young people with health and support needs?

Have you addressed the needs for information and support that young people might have around sexuality and sexual relationships?

Employment and other opportunities

Do your charging policies for community care services act as a barrier to paid employment?

Do health and social services commissioning strategies include working with employment services?

When commissioning and developing adult day services, do you aim to enable people to participate in their local communities? Are resources and support focused on tackling the barriers individuals face to doing the things they enjoy doing?

Transport and mobility

Do your commissioning strategies include access to transport and the provision of equipment to aid mobility?

Consultation and involvement

Are the views and experiences of young people with health and support needs sought during planning and commissioning? Are a variety of methods of consultation used?

144

References

Alberman, E., Nicholson, A. & Wald, A. (1992) *Severe Learning Disability in Young Children*. London: Wolfson Institute of Preventative Medicine.

aMAZE (1998) *Through the Maze: An information handbook for parents of children with special needs*. Brighton: aMaze (Community Base, 113–117 Queens Road, Brighton BN1 3XG).

Angele, M., Heard, R. & Kennedy, I. (1996) Lifelong learning – what a sham(e). *Education Journal*, (September).

Armitage, A. (1998) The role of a CF advocate. *Input*, (Autumn).

Atkin, K. & Ahmad, W. with Al-Falah (1998) *Ethnicity and Disability: The experience of young people with a sickle cell disorder or thalassaemia*. Centre for Research in Primary Care, University of Leeds.

Barnardo's Policy Development Unit (1996) *Transition to Adulthood*. Ilford: Barnardo's.

Barnes, H., Thornton, P. & Maynard Campbell, S. (1998) *Disabled People and Employment: A review of research and development work*. Bristol: Policy Press.

Beecher, W. (1998) *Growing Up: A guide to some information sources available to young disabled people and their families*. London: Council for Disabled Children.

Bennett, N. (1997) *Degrees of Difference*. Unpublished report for SKILL.

Blum, R. W. (1991) Overview of transition issues for youth with disabilities. *Paediatrician,* **18**, 101–104.

Brown, H. *et al.* (1994) Sexual abuse of adults with learning difficulties. *Social Care Research Findings*, **46**. York: Joseph Rowntree Foundation.

Brown, H., Croft-White, C., Wilson, C. & Stein, M. (forthcoming) *Taking the Initiative: Supporting the sexual rights of disabled people.* Brighton: Pavilion Publishing.

Bruce, I. W., McKennell, A. C. & Walker, E. C. (1992) *Blind and Partially Sighted People in Britain.* Vol. 2, Children. London: RNIB.

Caldwell, P. (1996) *Getting in Touch: Ways of working with people with severe learning disabilities and extensive support needs.* Brighton: Pavilion Publishing.

Caldwell, P. with Stevens, P. (1998) *Person to Person: Establishing contact and communication with people with profound learning disabilities and extra special needs.* Brighton: Pavilion Publishing.

Cavet, J. (1998) *People Don't Understand: Children, young people and their families living with a hidden disability.* London: National Children's Bureau.

Centre for Studies on Inclusive Education (1998) *A Trend Towards Inclusion: Statistics on special school placements and pupils with statements in ordinary schools, England 1992–96.* Bristol: CSIE.

Chamberlain, M. A., with Guthrie, S., Kettle, M. & Stowe, J. (1993) *An Assessment of Health and Related Needs of Physically Handicapped Young Adults.* London: HMSO.

Chamberlain, M. A. & Rooney, C. M. (1996) Young adults with arthritis: meeting their transitional needs. *British Journal of Rheumatology*, **35** (1) 84–90.

Closs, A. (1998) Quality of life of children and young people with serious medical conditions. In: Carol Robinson & Kirsten Stalker (Eds.) *Growing Up with Disability.* London: Jessica Kingsley Publishers.

Colby, J. (1994) The school child with ME. *British Journal of Special Education,* **21** (1) 9–11.

Cooper, S. A., Sharpe, K., Barrick, J. & Crowther, N. (1995) *The Housing Needs of People with Visual Impairment.* London: RNIB.

Cowen, A. (1996) *After Age 16 What Next? Services and benefits for young disabled people.* York: Family Fund Trust.

Crow, L. (1996) Including all of our lives: renewing the social model of disability. In: Jenny Morris (Ed.) *Encounters with Strangers: Feminism and disability.* London: The Women's Press.

Cunningham, G., Wilson, M. & Whiteley, S. (1998) *On Equal Terms: Supporting people with acquired brain injury in their own homes.* Bristol: Policy Press.

Department for Education and Employment/Department of Health (1996) *Supporting Pupils with Medical Needs.* London: Department for Education and Employment.

Department for Education, Department of Health and NHS Executive (1994) *The Education of Sick Children,* Circular 12/94. London: Department for Education.

Department of Health (1996) *Focus on Teenagers: Research into practice.* London: HMSO.

Department of Health (1997) *Better Services for Vulnerable People.* EL(97)62/C1(97)24. London: HMSO.

Department of Health (1998a) *Partnership in Action: New opportunities for joint working between health and social services.* London: Department of Health.

Department of Health (1998b) *Modernising Social Services.* Norwich: The Stationery Office.

Eiser, C. (1993) *Growing up with a Chronic Disease: The impact on children and their families.* London: Jessica Kingsley Publishers.

Emerson, E., McGill, P. & Mansell, J. (Eds.) (1994) *Severe Learning Disability and Challenging Behaviours: Designing high quality services.* London: Chapman and Hall.

Esmond, D. & Stewart, J. (1996) *Scope for Fair Housing: A literature review of housing with support for younger disabled people who require accessible housing.* London: Scope.

Family Fund Trust (1999) *After 16 – What's New? Choices and challenges for young disabled people.* York: Family Fund Trust.

Flynn, M. & Hirst, M. (1992) *This Year, Next Year, Sometime…? Learning disability and adulthood.* Manchester: National Development Team.

Fulford-Brown, D. (1999) *After 16 – What's new? Choices and challenges for young disabled people.* York: Family Fund Trust.

Further Education Funding Council (1996) *Inclusive Learning: Principles and recommendations – A summary of the findings of the Learning Difficulties and/or Disabilities Committee.* Coventry: Further Education Funding Council.

Harding, T. (1995) *The Sense Advocacy Project: An evaluation.* London: Sense – The National Deafblind and Rubella Association.

Hendey, N. (1998) *Young Adults and Disability: Transition to independent living?* Unpublished PhD Thesis, University of Nottingham.

Hirst, M. & Baldwin, S. (1994) *Unequal Opportunities: Growing up disabled.* London: HMSO.

148

Holman, A. & Collins, J. (1997) *Funding Freedom: Direct payments for people with learning difficulties.* London: Values into Action.

Holman, A. & Collins, J. (1998) Choice and control: making direct payments work for people with learning difficulties. In: Linda Ward (Ed.) *Innovations in Advocacy and Empowerment for People with Intellectual Disabilities.* Chorley, Lanchashire: Lisieux Hall Publications.

Kerr, M. (1998) Primary health care and health gain for people with a learning disability. *Tizard Learning Disability Review,* **3** (4) 6–14.

Kestenbaum, A. (1998) *Work, Rest and Pay: The deal for personal assistance users.* York : York Publishing Services.

Leak, A. M. (1994) The management of arthritis in adolescence. *British Journal of Rheumatology,* **33,** 882–888

Leighton Project (The) with Simon Grant & Daisy Cole (1998) Young people's aspirations. In: Carol Robinson & Kirsten Stalker (Eds.) *Growing Up with Disability.* London: Jessica Kingsley Publishers.

Marks, O. (1998) *Equipped for Equality.* London: Scope.

Martin, J., Meltzer, H. & Elliot, D. (1988) *OPCS Surveys of Disability in Great Britain: Report 1. The prevalence of disability among adults.* London: HMSO.

Miller, N. (1996) Together we Can Plan my Future: The needs of school leavers with a visual impairment and additional disabilities. Leatherhead: SeeAbility.

Morris, J. (1998a) *Still Missing? The experiences of disabled children and young people living away from their families.* London: The Who Cares? Trust.

Morris, J. (1998b) *Still Missing? Disabled children and the Children Act.* London: The Who Cares? Trust.

Morris, J. (1999) *Move on Up: Supporting young disabled people in their transition to adulthood.* London: Barnardo's.

Myers, M. (1995) A challenge to change: better services for people with challenging behaviour. In: Terry Philpot & Linda Ward (Eds.) *Values and Visions: Changing ideas in services for people with learning difficulties.* Oxford: Butterworth Heinemann.

Newham People First (1998) *Putting People First.* London Borough of Newham Social Services Department, People First and East London and City Health Authority.

Nottinghamshire County Council (1998) *Children with Disabilities in Nottinghamshire: Children and Young People's Disability Information Register: Service Report May 1995–March 1997.* Nottinghamshire County Council Social Services.

Noyes, J. (1999) *Voices and Choices. Young people who use assisted ventilation: their health and social care, and education.* London: The Stationery Office.

Olsen, R. & Sutton, J. (1996) *Adolescents with Diabetes: Their concerns about services.* Nuffield Community Care Studies Unit, University of Leicester.

Philpot, T. & Ward, L. (1995) *Values and Visions: Changing ideas in services for people with learning difficulties.* Oxford: Butterworth Heinemann.

Pownceby, J. (undated (a)) *The Coming of Age Project: A study of the transition from paediatric to adult care and treatment adherence amongst people with cystic fibrosis.* Bromley: Cystic Fibrosis Trust.

Pownceby, J. (undated (b)) *The Coming of Age Project: A study of the transition from paediatric to adult care and treatment adherence amongst people with cystic fibrosis.* Summary Report. Bromley: Cystic Fibrosis Trust.

Qureshi, H. (1994) The size of the problem. In: E. Emerson, P. McGill & J. Mansell (Eds.) *Severe Learning Disability and Challenging Behaviours: Designing high quality services.* London: Chapman and Hall.

Rhodes, A. with Lenehan, C. & Morrison, J. (1998) *Supporting Disabled Children who Need Invasive Clinical Procedures.* London: Barnardo's.

RNIB Focus Factsheet (undated) *Challenging behaviour in visually and learning disabled adults.* London: Royal National Institute for the Blind.

RNIB (1998, February) *Focus: A Newsletter for staff working with people with visual and learning disabilities.* London: Royal National Institute for the Blind.

RNIB Multiple Disability Services (1998) *Looking for eye problems in people with learning difficulties. Focus Factsheet.* London: Royal National Institute for the Blind.

Roberts, C. S., Turney, M. E. & Knowles, A. M. (1998) Pyschosocial issues of adolescents with cancer. *Social Work in Health Care,* **27** (4) 3–18.

Russell, P. (1996) *Rites of Passage: Transition to adult life for young disabled people.* London: Council for Disabled Children.

Ryan, T. (1997) *Making Our Own Way: Transition from school to adulthood in the lives of people who have learning difficulties.* London: Values into Action.

Ryan, T. (1998) *The Cost of Opportunity: Purchasing strategies in the housing and support arrangements of people with learning difficulties.* London: Values into Action.

Sanderson, H. (1998) A say in my future: involving people with profound and multiple disabilities in person centred planning. In: Linda Ward (Ed.) *Innovations in Advocacy and Empowerment for People with Intellectual Disabilities.* Chorley, Lanchashire: Lisieux Hall Publications.

Sebba, J. with Sachdev, D. (1997) *What Works in Inclusive Education?* London: Barnardo's.

Simons, K. (1998) *Home, Work and Inclusion: The social policy implications of supporting living and employment for people with learning disabilities.* York: York Publishing Services.

Social Services Inspectorate (1992) *Whose Life is it Anyway?* London: Department of Health.

Social Services Inspectorate (1995a) *Growing Up and Moving On: Report of an SSI project on transition services for disabled young people.* London: Department of Health.

Social Services Inspectorate (1995b) *Planning for Life: Developing community service for people with multiple disabilities.* London: Department of Health.

Social Services Inspectorate (1995c) *Opportunities or Knocks: National inspection of recreation and leisure in day services for people with learning difficulties.* London: Department of Health.

Social Services Inspectorate (1996a) *Searching for Service: An inspection of service responses made to the needs of disabled young adults and their carers.* London: Department of Health.

Social Services Inspectorate (1996b) *Planning for Life: Developing community services for people with complex multiple disabilities – No. 2 Good Practice in Manchester.* London: Department of Health.

Social Services Inspectorate (1997a) *Moving on Towards Independence: Second report of an SSI project on transition services for disabled young people.* London: Department of Health.

Social Services Inspectorate (1997b) *'A Hidden Disability': Report of the SSI Traumatic Brain Injury Rehabilitation Project.* London: Social Services Inspectorate.

Spastics Society (1978) *Report of the Working Party to discuss the special needs of handicapped adolescents.* London: Spastics Society (now Scope).

Stevenson, C. J., Pharoah, P. O. D. & Stevenson, R. (1997) Cerebral palsy – the transition from youth to adulthood. *Developmental Medicine and Child Neurology*, **39**, 336–342.

Stone, E., Mercer, G. & Barnes, C. (1998) *The Snowden Survey 1998.* Snowden Award Scheme.

Sutcliffe, J. & Jacobsen, Y. (1998a) Continuing education and equal opportunities for adults with learning difficulties. *Findings*, November. York: Joseph Rowntree Foundation.

Sutcliffe, J. & Jacobsen, Y. (1998b) *All Things Being Equal? A practical guide to widening participation for adults with learning difficulties in adult education.* NIACE.

Thapar, A. K. (1996) Care of patients with epilepsy in the community: will new initiatives address old problems? *British Journal of General Practice.*

Ward, L. (Ed.) (1998) *Innovations in Advocacy and Empowerment for People with Intellectual Disabilities.* Chorley, Lancashire: Lisieux Hall Publications.

Wilson, J. (1998) The NHS that people with long-term illness want. *King's Fund News*, **21** (2) 6.

Young Adults Transition Project (1998a) *Working Paper 1: Profile of disabled school leavers in Lewisham and Southwark.* Optimum Health Services NHS Trust.

Young Adults Transition Project (1998b) *Working Paper 2: Professionals' views of transition planning.* Optimum Health Services NHS Trust.